THE GREATEST FLIGHT

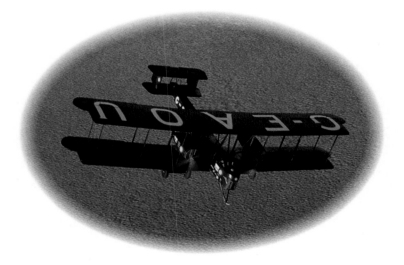

We anxious watchers at Fannie Bay at last
saw the Vimy appear as a little speck away towards
the Timor Sea and then grow larger and larger as
it circled the ground and landed.

It was one of the most moving sights
I can remember—the termination of
one of the greatest flights, if not the
greatest, in the history of aviation…
for no one had ever flown across
the world before.

SIR HUDSON FYSH
45 YEARS AFTER FOUNDING QANTAS AIRWAYS,
RECALLING ROSS AND KEITH SMITH'S ARRIVAL IN
AUSTRALIA AFTER THEIR HISTORIC FLIGHT FROM
LONDON, DECEMBER 10, 1919

The members of the Vimy 19/94 project would like to express their gratitude to the two main sponsors, who had the same vision back in 1919, when they supported the original Vimy flight by Ross and Keith Smith and their crew:

THE NATIONAL GEOGRAPHIC SOCIETY
SHELL INTERNATIONAL

We also offer our sincere thanks to the following organizations, who were critical to the success of the 1994 flight:

THE AUSTRALIAN ARMY AVIATION CORPS
THE BAHRAIN COMMITTEE
GIEVES & HAWKES
GULF AIR
POLICE AVIATION SERVICES, UK
QANTAS
UNITED STATES AIR FORCE
USAIG
WELDON OWEN PUBLISHING

RELIVING THE AERIAL TRIUMPH THAT CHANGED THE WORLD

THE GREATEST FLIGHT

PETER MCMILLAN

PHOTOGRAPHS BY JAMES L. STANFIELD

HISTORICAL TEXT BY TERRY GWYNN-JONES

CONSTRUCTION TEXT BY JOHN LA NOUE

FOREWORD BY WALTER J. BOYNE

Turner Publishing, Inc.

ATLANTA

Published by Turner Publishing, Inc.
A Subsidiary of Turner Broadcasting System, Inc.
1050 Techwood Drive N.W.
Atlanta, Georgia 30318

Distributed by Andrews and McMeel
A Universal Press Syndicate Company
4900 Main Street
Kansas City, Missouri 64112

Conceived and produced by Weldon Owen Pty Limited
43 Victoria Street, McMahons Point NSW 2060, Australia
Fax (61 2) 929 8352
A Member of the Weldon Owen Group of Companies
Sydney • San Francisco • London

Weldon Owen
Chairman: Kevin Weldon
President: John Owen
Publisher: Sheena Coupe
Editorial Director: Annette Carter
Copy Editors: Annette Carter and Julian Leatherdale
Historical Picture Research: Joanna Collard
Art Director and Designer: Mark Nichols
Associate Designers: Denny Allnutt and Gary Humphrys
Computer Layout: Veronica Hilton
Map: Kenn Backhaus
Vice President, International Sales: Stuart Laurence
Coeditions Director: Derek Barton
Production Consultant: Mick Bagnato
Production Manager: Simone Perryman

First Edition 10 9 8 7 6 5 4 3 2 1

Library of Congress Cataloging-in-Publication Data
McMillan, Peter.
    The greatest flight: reliving the aerial triumph that changed the world / by Peter McMillan, John La Noue, and Terry Gwynn-Jones.—1st ed.
        p. cm.
    Includes index.
    ISBN 1-57036-238-6 (alk. paper)
        1. Aeronautics—Flights. 2. McMillan, Peter—Journeys. 3. La Noue, John—Journeys. 4. Vimy (Bomber)—History. I. La Noue, John. II. Gwynn-Jones, Terry, 1933– III. Title.
TL721.M35M38 1995
629.13'09—dc20
                                                    95-19018
                                                    CIP

Manufactured by Mandarin Offset
Printed in Hong Kong

A WELDON OWEN PRODUCTION

The publisher gratefully acknowledges the assistance of The National Geographic Society in the production of this book.

PROJECT TEAM

PATRON
HRH Prince Michael of Kent

PROJECT DIRECTOR/VIMY PILOT
Peter McMillan

OPERATIONS DIRECTOR/VIMY PILOT
Lang Kidby

PROJECT MANAGER
Logistics/Events/Public Relations
Tessa Barroll

PROJECT COORDINATOR
Bev Kidby

FINANCE
Elaine Tanaka, Treasurer
Mike Bittner, Accountant
Elise Wen, Adviser

FLIGHT OPERATIONS DIRECTOR
Mark Rebholz

NOMAD PILOT
Mick Reynolds

ISLANDER PILOT
Ian Snell

SUPPORT PLANE CREWS
Gary Tierney, Nomad Copilot
Bob Shaw, Nomad Engineer
Malcolm Wood, Second Islander Pilot
Mark Rebholz, Islander Copilot
Erik Durfey, Australian Support
Kevin Weldon, Australian Helicopter
    Support

VIMY TEST PILOTS
Peter Hoar, Test Flight Supervisor
Dizzy Addicott, Test Flight Adviser

FUEL/LUBRICANT
SUPPLY AND LOGISTICS
Andy Morrison, Shell International

AIRCRAFT CONSTRUCTION
United States
John La Noue, Chief Engineer
Dan Nelson, Senior Fabricator

Australia
Wayne Daley, Chief Engineer
Bill Whitney, Designer

NATIONAL GEOGRAPHIC
FIELD TEAM
James L. Stanfield, Photographer
Joe Stancampiano, Photographic
    Engineer
Chris Weber, Television Producer
Bob Poole, Cinematographer
Mark Roy, Sound Engineer

NATIONAL GEOGRAPHIC
SUPPORT TEAM
Jenny Moseley, UK
Barbara Moffet
Mary Smith
Peter Miller
Val Mattingley, UK
Ros Collin, UK
David Todd, UK
Larry Nighswander
Maria Bunai
Caitlin Wargo
Bob Sims
Benita Swash
Neva Folk
Stella Cha

PUBLICITY AND FUND-RAISING
Tessa Barroll
Bev Kidby
Roni Lord, Australia
Pam Seaborn, Australia
Joanna Gill, Australia
Raymond Salisbury-Jones, UK
Bill Patterson
Chris and Carey Condy
Colin Lind
Pat Healy
Perfect Relations, India
Guy Edwards
Pamela Callaghan

The support of the following organizations and individuals is gratefully acknowledged:

SHELL INTERNATIONAL
London
Lawrie Austin
Iain Everingham
Mike Brannigan
Jackie Ireland
Andy Morrison
Andrew McEachern
Andrew Vickers
Robert French

Field Support
Giovanni Acbano, Italy
Alexis Laskaris, Greece
Dr. Graeme Sweeney, Egypt
O. T. Levent, PASCO, Saudi Arabia
John Mills, Oman
Thomas V. Higgins, Pakistan
Vikram Mehta, India
Ratan Dayal, India
Atul Bindal, India
Ponlend Kositwongsakul, Thailand
Melvyn Louis, Malaysia
Teoh Eng Hong, Singapore
Fong Cheng Kee, Singapore
David Tyler, Indonesia
Bambang Harayadi, Indonesia
Paul Ulrick, Australia
Daniel Prokop, Australia

WELDON OWEN PUBLISHING
Kevin Weldon
John Owen
Roni Lord
Dawn Low
Sigrid Chase
Jim Obata
Patty Hill
Angela Williams
John Bull

Richard Van Oosterhout
Beverley Sharpe
Anne Kinchin

THE BAHRAIN COMMITTEE
His Excellency Yousuf Ahmed
    Al Shirawi
Shaikh Hamad bin Ebrahim Al Khalifa
David Ryan
Ibrahim Al Hamar
Shaikh Mohamed bin Khalifa al Khalifa
Anne Hendrie
Shaikh Hamad bin Mohamed Al Khalifa
Major Nagi Al Hashel
Mohamed Ali Salem
Mirza Abdul Rasool Al Ali

GULF AIR
His Excellency Salim bin
    Ali Nasser Assiyabi
Captain J. R. Taylor
Abdul Rahman Al Busaidy
Captain Abdul Rehman Al Gaoud
Leslie Britton
Peter Lowden, London
David Nicholas, London
Caroline White, London

USAIG
Harold Clarke
Dave McKay
Dick McGreal
David Law
Bill Tillotson (RHH, Los Angeles)

THE AUSTRALIAN ARMY
Colonel Peter Simpson
Major Mick Reynolds
Sergeant Harri Keinonen
Officers and men of the First Aviation
    Regiment, Oakey, Queensland

POLICE AVIATION SERVICES
United Kingdom
Ian Snell
Malcolm Wood
Mark Trumble
Jim Whittaker

BROOKLANDS MUSEUM
Morag Barton, Museum Director
Sir Peter Masefield
Julian Temple
John Pulford
Spud Borer
Steve Deveraux
Peter Westacott
Keith Griggs
Linda Sommerville
Keith Harris
Alan Aylieff
Brooklands staff and volunteers

GIEVES & HAWKES
Robert Gieve
Garry Beverley
Amanda Hutchinson

QANTAS
Warwick Tainton
Ray Heineger
Bob Bailey
Jim Eames
Mike Cottee
Tessa Wood

BRUNTONS (MUSSELBURGH) LTD.
Andrew Stevenson
Ken Lydall

SOCIETY OF BRITISH AEROSPACE COMPANIES/FARNBOROUGH '94
Paul Cope
Helene Cox
Keith Gordon

Sally Hughes
Martin Fiddler
Mike Spick
John Blake
Bell Helicopters, Inc.

FEDERAL AVIATION ADMINISTRATION
United States
Del Ott

CIVIL AVIATION AUTHORITY
United Kingdom
Barry Tempest
Derek Fautley
Ron Saull
P. W. Doolan

CIVIL AVIATION AUTHORITY
Australia
Rick Davies

BBC
Sean Maffett
Rod Sharpe

UNITED STATES AIR FORCE
Colonel D. Pope
Caroll Clifford
Lieutenant Colonel Dan Nichols
Captain Victor Hines
Sergeant Cathy Landroche
John Ware
Don Lopez, National Air and Space
    Museum
Volunteers at RAF Mildenhall

HAMILTON FIELD/SIXTH UNITED STATES ARMY
Colonel Renn
Colonel Janacek
Dixie Porter
Severin Johnson

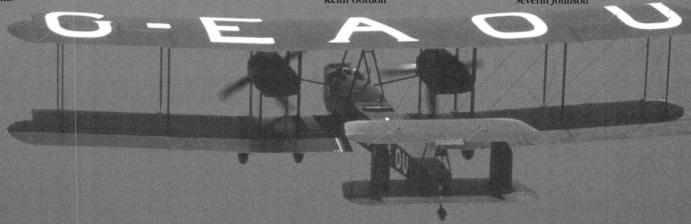

Endpapers
In the early morning light of the Australian outback, the Vimy pushes southward over a cattle station in the Northern Territory.

Pages 2–3
October 9, 1994: Two thousand feet above the Java Sea, Peter McMillan (right) grips the wheel while Lang Kidby checks the map. The Vimy has just crossed the equator. On December 6, 1919, her predecessor was the first aircraft ever to cross the line that divides the hemispheres.

Pages 4–5
A close-up view of the forward crew positions, ahead of the World War I bomber's massive wings and between her 11-foot propellers.

Pages 6–7
The Vimy makes a farewell flyby for the many Arabian friends who came to see her in the desert of Bahrain.

Pages 8–9
On October 22, 1994, forty-two days after leaving England, the Vimy speeds toward victory at Darwin. After seven hours over the Timor Sea, the crew anxiously await the sight of Australia.

Pages 10–11
On her tour of Australia, G-EAOU passes over the city of Melbourne on February 25, 1920. The pilots, Ross and Keith Smith, are national heroes and have been made Knights of the British Empire by King George V.

Page 14
The Vimy's huge propellers pull her across the lunar-like terrain that marks the border between Iran and Pakistan. There are several hours of this treacherous landscape to go before the crew will reach Karachi.

Pages 16–17
At Cairo, the Vimy is grounded by a dense layer of fog blanketing the Nile Valley. In Egypt, as throughout her journey, the huge box kite attracted children like a magnet.

CONTENTS

FOREWORD

THE SEVENTY-FIFTH ANNIVERSARY reenactment of Ross and Keith Smith's pioneering flight from England to Australia is one of the most refreshing flying events of the twentieth century, ranking with the original voyage and with such modern-day counterparts as the round-the-world flight of the *Voyager* as a tonic for the aviation world.

This exciting project, mammoth in its scope and so daring in its undertaking, was made possible by the vision of a few men of courage who recreated not just a flight but also the whole climate of adventure that characterized the early days of aviation. American Peter McMillan and Australian Lang Kidby piloted the aircraft and managed the entire project, in all its financial, engineering, managerial and aerodynamic complexity. But they are the first to attribute the success of the mission to the efforts of their loyal and devoted team. McMillan and Kidby prevailed over the multiplicity of obstacles in the path of the project, just as they overcame the engineering problems implicit in recreating an aircraft designed during World War I.

They achieved success in abundance, first with the aircraft itself, an absolutely beautiful recreation of the World War I bomber that made not one but two immensely significant flights—the first nonstop flight across the Atlantic, and the first flight halfway around the world, from London to Australia. I was fortunate to see the Vimy while it was under construction, and can attest to the extraordinary craftsmanship that went into building it and its amazing fidelity to the original aircraft.

Their flight was equally successful, overcoming all of the hazards encountered seventy-five years ago, plus some modern ones, including a hair-raising forced landing in Sumatra. This book is the tangible expression of that success, and, in conjunction with the magazine, television and film coverage of the event, will further inflame the sense of excitement and adventure that this modern epic flight has engendered.

We have all become accustomed to the sterile, encapsulated boredom of jet transport, passing with indifference over ocean or land at near-sonic speeds. McMillan and Kidby were out in the wind, 300 feet low and 75 miles per hour slow, able to experience travel as it once was, letting the terrain unfold below, drinking in the sights and sounds and smells of the hugely diverse environments of the world, beautiful and terrifying—just as Ross and Keith Smith had done three-quarters of a century before. Ah, that we too could do it! In this book, we can stow away.

But perhaps the most important aspect of the entire operation is one that harks back to the very first flyers, to the daring airmen of both world wars, to test pilots of every nation, and to the astronauts—that glorious sense of daring, and the willingness to risk all on the outcome of a hazardous but worthwhile undertaking. At a time when some generations are worrying about job security, and others, even younger, about social security, Peter McMillan and Lang Kidby cast off from ordinary concerns and pitted themselves against the odds. They won gloriously—as you'll discover within the pages of this magnificent book.

Walter J. Boyne

Walter J. Boyne
Author/Historian
Former Director of the National Air and Space Museum

Start
Hounslow Heath (now Heathrow):
November 12, 1919
Farnborough: September 11, 1994

FARNBOROUGH
ENGLAND
LONDON

E U R O P E

F R A N C E

TROYES
CHALON-SUR-SAÔNE
MENDE
CANNES
LYON
PISA
VENTURINA
ROME
ITALY
TARANTO
Acropolis
ATHENS
GREECE

Storms and mountains
force a westward
diversion to Mende

CRETE
CANEA   DAMASCUS

EUPHRATES
RIVER
TIGRIS
SYRIA

M E D I T E R R A N E A N
S E A

ALEXANDRIA

AR RAMADI
(RAMADIE)

November 25, 1919: 5,790 miles
September 28, 1994: 5,952 miles

Longest leg (miles):
Bandar Abbas to Karachi
730 miles, 8 hours and 30 minutes

Longest leg (mile
Delhi to Calcutta
742 miles, 10 hou
and 10 minutes

A S I A

Pyramids of Giza
Cairo

E G Y P T

IRAQ

BASRA

Nafud Desert

Ha'il

PERSIAN
GULF

IRAN
(PERSIA)

P A K I S T A N

INDUS

YAMUNA
RIVER

DELHI

ALLAHABAD

BANG

CALCU

SAUDI ARABIA
(ARABIA)

BAHRAIN

BANDAR
ABBAS

KARACHI

Gulf of
Oman

MATHURA
(MUTTRA)

Taj Mahal

AGRA

MUSCAT
OMAN

The Vimy makes a desert
landing in Bahrain as part
of festivities hosted by the
government.

ARABIAN SEA

I N D I A

BAY
BENGA

N I L E

RED SEA

A F R I C A

BLACK SEA

CASPIAN
SEA

1919 ROUTE AND STOP (28 DAYS TO DARWIN)
1994 ROUTE AND STOP (42 DAYS TO DARWIN)
PLACES WHERE BOTH FLIGHTS LANDED
HISTORICAL NAMES ARE SHOWN IN PARENTHESES
SCALE VARIES IN THIS PROJECTION.

E

I N D I A N   O C E A N

BACKHAUS

VICKERS VIMY
1919 · 1994

MYANMAR (BURMA)

THAILAND (SIAM)

An engine begins missing badly over Thailand. The crew divert to Langkawi island, where repairs are improvised with a motorcycle spark plug.

PACIFIC OCEAN

BANGKOK

Yangon (Rangoon)

GULF OF THAILAND

Songkhla (Singora)

Langkawi Penang Sitiawan

MALAYSIA (MALAYA)

SINGAPORE

BORNEO

INDONESIA (DUTCH EAST INDIES)

NEW GUINEA

SUMATRA

Atambua (Atamboea)

TIMOR

Arrival in Darwin
December 10, 1919: 11,060 miles
October 22, 1994: 11,374 miles

Kalijati (Kaledjat)

BIMA

Darwin

Warlock Ponds

Seventy-five years later, the Vimy crew find fuel cans near Charleville left behind by the Smiths and their mechanics.

Palembang

Jakarta (Batavia) JAVA

Surabaya (Soerabaya)

BALI

SUMBAWA

Kupang

SEA

Newcastle Waters

CRASH SITE
In dense smoke over Sumatra, the right engine sputters to a stop. The crew make a harrowing emergency landing in a rice paddy, and the Vimy is grounded for six days.

Tennant Creek

Cloncurry

Longreach

Charleville

Oakey

Brisbane

Coffs Harbour

Bourke

AUSTRALIA

Sydney

Cootamundra

Henty

Mittagong

Melbourne

The Vimy crew complete the journey in Adelaide, the Smith brothers' home town, where the original G-EAOU is on display at the airport.

Adelaide

MAYDAY!
SUMATRA, INDONESIA
OCTOBER 9, 1994

Previous page: The Vickers Vimy plows at 75 miles per hour through the endless blanket of smoke over the Indonesian island of Sumatra. Nil visibility is a deadly problem: even worse is the right engine, which is groaning in final agony.

Above: Heavy smoke forces the giant biplane to skim perilously low over the inhospitable jungle, which is burning out of control. Should her ailing motor give up, the Vimy will crash helplessly into the dense vegetation in just a few moments.

IT WAS LIKE A DREAM—more like a nightmare. The pungent smoke made the inferno beneath even more surreal, as if I were looking at the fiery jungle through a bowl of murky water. Our fate—or perhaps our epitaph—was down there, 2,000 feet below. But the waiting would be over soon enough. We were fluttering down like a huge kite without a string. The Vimy's right engine had failed over the remote and inhospitable island called Sumatra.

"Mayday, Mayday, Mayday. Vimy One, Vimy One, Vimy One. We've had an engine failure," Lang called out to anyone listening on the radio. "We're making an emergency landing." No response.

"See any place to land?" I yelled, as I struggled to counteract the asymmetric torque.

"There's a small airfield twenty-five miles away," he said, scanning a map.

"We'll never make it." The muscles of my left leg were trembling as I held the rudder against the overwhelming momentum to the right. Even with the left engine operating, the Vimy was descending at 150 feet per minute.

Lang turned in the cramped confines of the cockpit. "What about that road on the left?" he said, pointing to a dirt lane cutting through a paddy field.

I strained to see it through the haze of smoke, and fought to bring the nose around to the left, which brought us down much faster. The road looked too narrow to me, and it was directly across wind. But there weren't many choices—only the little dirt path, the burning jungle, or the rice paddies interlaced with menacing retaining walls only 20 yards apart.

Jim Stanfield, our photographer from National Geographic, popped up from his seat in the nose. He snapped a few pictures of the motionless prop, but he was blocking my view. "Jim, not now!" I yelled. "We're about to crash!" He disappeared.

As we descended through 200 feet, I could see well enough to know we were headed for disaster. The road before us was only half the width we needed, and there was a big blue dumptruck full of soil smack in the middle. As we bore down on them, several boys on bicycles dived headfirst into the deep ditches along the roadside.

"We can't use the road," I shouted, almost simultaneously giving full power to the left engine. This pitched the nose up and swung us sharply to the right. Pulling the wheel with both hands, I tried to level the wings to stop us from cartwheeling. We braced for impact.

Latitude 4°42'S, longitude 105°16'E
"Mayday, Mayday, Mayday." Disaster strikes when the starboard engine fails at 3:12 p.m. Wounded, the Vimy is going down. American Peter McMillan (right) struggles to control the unwieldy aircraft while he and Australian copilot Lang Kidby search desperately for a place to land. There is no response to Lang's distress calls on the radio. Seventy-five years earlier, in 1919, another Vickers Vimy just like this one flew over this spot on the way to completing the first flight halfway around the world, from London to Australia. The modern-day attempt to relive the historic achievement looks like it will end abruptly, on the scrubby terrain 2,000 feet below.

GENESIS:
TO BUILD A DREAM

HISTORIANS STUDY the past; archaeologists dig up the past. But I'm not sure what you call those who relive the past. In most cases, I suppose they would be called daydreamers. That is what I am. I often drift away in search of the sights and sounds and smells of the past. The past is full of brave men and women who shaped our world, but most of them are forgotten. Were they ordinary people, oblivious of the risks they took? Or did they deliberately go out to meet danger, realizing that valor might reap benefits for themselves and for others? I want to meet them. Maybe I can build a sort of time machine to go back and experience their deeds. But even with such a time machine, I can never answer the real question: could I have been one of them?

Above: Peter McMillan (left) and Lang Kidby check the engine gauges on the Vimy's port side as the sun retreats over the Indonesian island of Sumbawa. The two pilots share a passion for the great flying heroes of the past and the sturdy ships they flew.

Left: The partially painted biplane casts a long shadow in the early morning Californian light as the builders use surveying equipment to check the accuracy of the rigging.

Far left: Builder Dan Nelson sits in the raw-plywood nose cockpit, a cramped position he will become all too familiar with in the months ahead.

Above: Seen through the box kite's tail and her complex web of external bracing wires, workers make adjustments to the engine mounts. The latticework may look flimsy compared to the streamlined shape of modern aircraft, but in fact the Vimy is sturdily built, having been designed for the missions of war and unimproved fields of seventy-five years ago.

Above: Lang Kidby checks for excessive vibration during engine testing. Precise balancing of the huge, four-bladed propellers proved to be a critical task.

Below: The reduction gearbox designed for the Vimy replica is just behind the propeller. This device allowed modern engines to be mated with antique-style propellers.

Flight has always been the stuff of dreams, even back as far as the ancient Greeks and the myth of Icarus. But what was the greatest flight? Who was the greatest pilot, and what sort of craft did he fly? This could be the subject of a lengthy debate. It was for me and my friend and fellow dreamer Lang Kidby in December 1992.

THE GREATEST FLIGHT

Lang and I discussed Lindbergh, the Wright brothers, Blériot and other pioneers of flight, but in the end we agreed. Greatest of all was Captain Ross Smith, who in 1919 flew a Vickers Vimy biplane halfway around the world in twenty-eight days—the first flight from London to Australia. That may not sound impressive in an age when the same distance is covered by ordinary travelers in less than a day, but it was his achievement more than any other that silenced the skeptics and proved that airplanes would change the way we live by bringing the peoples of the world together to an unprecedented extent.

But this audacious journey, which joined the outposts of the British Empire over a largely uncharted route, was very much a team effort. Ross Smith had the indispensable support of his navigator brother, Keith, and two tireless mechanics, Wally Shiers and Jim Bennett. Their Vimy airplane was worthy as well. One just like it, flown by Englishmen

John Alcock and Arthur Whitten-Brown, had recently made the first flight across the Atlantic. The mammoth biplane and these brave pioneers set the stage for a time when hopping across continents would be not much harder than riding across town on a bus.

Ah, to build a Vimy and travel back in time seventy-five years—that really was a dream!

Like any great adventure, this one began with an idea. There were many peaks and troughs over the next two years, and the only thing never in doubt was our determination to live out our dream. As Lang and I stood against the railing of a Brisbane ferry, looking at the coast of Australia, it sounded so grand

Left: The setting sun glints off the upper wing as the Vimy recalls aviation's most glamorous and dangerous era, setting the leisurely pace of 75 miles per hour on this test flight over northern California. Peter and Lang took turns at becoming familiar with the leaden controls. Handling her was as much like weightlifting as it was like flying. But there was no mistaking that solid, stately feel—though newborn, she was truly a ship from the past.

Below: Test flights continued after the Vimy was shipped to England. The big green beast proved rather more temperamental in the blustery skies of East Anglia.

and so simple. "We'll build a Vimy and fly it from England to Australia," he said. "Just in time for the seventy-fifth anniversary in 1994," I added confidently. "But where do we start?"

BLUEPRINTS FOR ADVENTURE

I returned to the United States, enthralled by the possibility of masterminding the world's greatest time-travel adventure. After a few phone calls to the leading authorities on World War I aircraft, I was directed all the way back to Brisbane and an aircraft engineer named Bill Whitney. Bill, I was told, had designed a full-scale replica of the *Southern Cross*, an enormous trimotor from 1928. I called Lang, and he paid a visit to Bill, who lived just across town from him.

"Where in the world would we find a set of plans for a Vickers Vimy?" Lang asked. Bill bent down and pulled

a large black binder from his bottom drawer. He dropped it on his desk with a thump. "Right here," he said, with a broad smile. "I've been dreaming of building a Vimy for years. I copied these off some microfilm from the Royal Air Force Museum in England just in case some mad fools wanted to build one."

A BIG BITE

It was providence. It was a miracle. We had found the only set of Vimy plans in the world. But now came the bad news. Bill estimated that to convert these scratchy pages into a set of working blueprints, to fill in the gaps, and to do the required analysis would cost more than $100,000. That was just for the paper. What about the lumber, fabric, steel, engines, propellers and the other tens of thousands of parts? I put up the funding

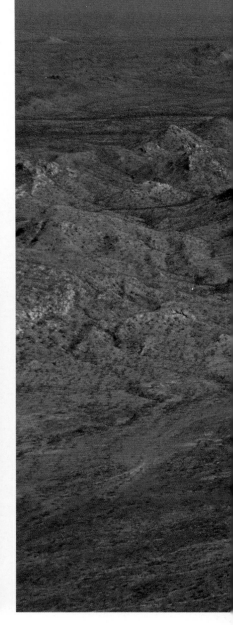

to get the project underway in the hope that we would later find sponsors to ease the financial burden.

We had to start somewhere, and we had to start now. We had to work fast and not agonize over our mistakes. We had only eighteen months to build the largest-ever replica aircraft.

Little did we know that the task would involve over 4,000 pages of new drawings, more than 20,000 man-hours of labor and $1.5 million. Such is the price of building a time machine, but the greatest flight was going to happen—again.

Just as for Ross Smith and his crew, there would be countless hazards along the way, natural and mechanical. We would experience torrential rains, hail and sandstorms, fog and blinding smoke. We would alternately be chilled or baked for hours on end in the cramped confines of our open cockpit. We had a near-miss with an outbreak of plague. A failed engine brought us down in a scrubby field on one of the world's remotest islands. But through all these perils, I truly traveled back in time and had the privilege to come to know the great hero whose adventurous spirit had such a profound effect on the way we move around the modern world. His name rightfully belongs alongside those of Magellan, Columbus, Captain Cook and even the Apollo astronauts: Captain Sir Ross Smith.

The story of Ross Smith's daring feat is retold in the following pages, as the indispensable prelude to the modern-day adventure it inspired—probably the greatest adventure of our lives.

PETER McMILLAN, 1994

Above and left: Long hours were spent in the windy open cockpit as the Vimy made her way across the world. The terrain was sometimes rugged and barren, sometimes flat and lush, but there was always time to give the Earth a good, long look and to think about a time when it seemed a much bigger place.

Opposite page, left: A weathered plaque marks the spot where, in December 1919, Ross Smith and his crew were forced down near Charleville, in Queensland. The Vimy was crossing inland Australia after her monumental voyage from England, halfway around the world. It was here that the modern flyers would touch their heroes.

THE GREAT
TRANS-PLANET
AIR RACE

THE GREAT TRANS-PLANET AIR RACE

TERRY GWYNN-JONES

*"First Europe, and then the globe,
will be linked by flight…"*

CLAUDE GRAHAM WHITE
AND HARRY HARPER

THE YEAR 1919 was a turning point in aviation history, and a year of high adventure. It triggered a remarkable twenty years of aerial pioneering between the two world wars that took the aeroplane out of the realm of fingers-crossed barnstorming and into the era of the great airlines. In the first decade of powered flight, before World War I, few aviators had dared to fly their cantankerous machines any great distance across country, let alone across water. In the public mind, the airplane remained the domain of thrill-seekers, and was seen as an unreliable contraption that frequently crashed in demonstrations at air shows and country fairs.

Left: Captain Ross Smith, AFC (standing, left), and his crew inspect the cockpit of their Vickers Vimy F.B.27A at Brooklands, in England, in October 1919. Conceived late in 1917, the prototype Vimy was designed, built and test-flown in just four months. Its role was to meet urgent British requirements for a long-range tactical bomber to retaliate for the night bombing of Britain by German aircraft. World War I ended, however, before Vimys saw action.

Below: In 1913, another French airman made a remarkable international flight. Flying a Morane-Saulnier Type 1 monoplane, Roland Garros made a 453-mile crossing of the Mediterranean, from Saint-Raphael, in southern France, to Bizerte, in Tunisia. Slowed by headwinds, he became anxious when landfall was overdue. "I didn't know if my fuel would last," Garros recalled. He landed after 7 hours and 53 minutes—with just 7 minutes' fuel remaining!

Left: The first international over-water flight took place in 1909, when French pioneer Louis Blériot flew 22 miles over the English Channel, from Calais to Dover. Blériot's flimsy monoplane had just enough power to climb over Dover's famed White Cliffs (right) before crash-landing near Dover Castle. The flight evoked unprecedented public attention. "Britain's impregnability has passed away," a newspaper declared.

Far left: A letter carried on the first flight from England to Australia for postage in Australia.

AVIATION'S EARLY DAYS

Perhaps the outstanding difficulty in those early years was keeping the airframes and engines working. Reliability was so marginal. Bits kept busting and falling off. There were no tried and tested aircraft materials or parts as there are today.... We used bits and pieces from carpenters shops and ships chandlers like cables and turnbuckles in our airframes, but because we subjected them to strange forces and environments they sometimes failed.... We screwed, stuck and bolted them together as best we knew how. When they broke we tried again if we were lucky enough to survive the landing. It was a never ending struggle....But the spirit of adventure was wonderful. The good humour was infectious.

SIR THOMAS SOPWITH

Above: In 1910, Calbraith Rogers set out from New York on a $50,000 transcontinental challenge. He survived fifteen accidents and rebuilt his Wright biplane five times before reaching Long Beach, California, with a broken leg. The 4,250-mile odyssey took eighty-four days, and only the rudder and engine sump remained of the original airplane.

Below: The world leader in early aircraft design, France produced this sleek 1912 Deperdussin Monocoupe racer. Piloted by Jules Védrines, it was the first airplane to exceed 100 miles per hour. In 1913, Védrines flew the 2,500 miles from Paris to Cairo in a Blériot monoplane.

Above: Aviation came of age at the world's first air show, held at Reims, France, in 1909. Half a million people attended, including royalty, politicians and European society.

Sir Thomas Sopwith, British pioneer pilot and one of the world's great aircraft builders, was well acquainted with the hazards of that experimental prewar period. In an interview given in 1983, late in his life, he reminisced:

Perhaps the outstanding difficulty in those early years was keeping the airframes and engines working. Reliability was so marginal. Bits kept busting and falling off. There were no tried and tested aircraft materials or parts as there are today. We adapted components from motor car engines and those were not even reliable on the road let alone in the air.

We used bits and pieces from carpenters shops and ships chandlers like cables and turnbuckles in our airframes, but because we subjected them to strange forces and environments they sometimes failed....We screwed, stuck and bolted them together as best we knew how. When they broke we tried again if we were lucky enough to survive the landing.

It was a never ending struggle....But the spirit of adventure was wonderful. The good humour was infectious. And as we got better and better at flying it was natural that the adventurous companies and individuals wanted to prove themselves.

But the vision to succeed was there. Even as early as 1914, bold predictions were being made. In their book *The Aeroplane*, British pilot Claude Grahame-White and aviation journalist Harry Harper stated: *First Europe, and then the globe, will be linked by flight, and nations so knit together that they will grow to be next door neighbours. This conquest of the air will prove, ultimately, to be man's greatest and most glorious triumph. What railways have done for nations, airways will do for the world.*

WAR AND PEACE

The pursuit of this grand vision was interrupted by the war and was not resumed until 1919. But the war had played a crucial part in the development of aviation, providing a spur to rapid improvements in aircraft design and to the establishment of a production-line manufacturing industry. Perhaps more important, the airplane—no longer the plaything of amateurs —had been given a raison d'être. The crude, unpredictable machines of aviation's faltering early years had been refined by the needs of combat. At the war's end, comparatively reliable machines able to fly 500 miles at cruising speeds approaching 100 miles per hour were commonplace.

With the coming of peace, those connected with the young aviation industry were well aware that its future lay with transportation. But they now faced a new battle: convincing tunnel-visioned bureaucrats, and a doubting public, that the airplane could become a safe and respectable passenger vehicle of the future.

The curtain was about to rise on a twenty-year aerial extravaganza. Its star performers—pilots, navigators and mechanics—would risk nothing less than their lives to bridge the oceans and shrink the globe until the continents would be no more than a day apart.

Captain Ross Smith, AFC (left), and his observer, Lieutenant E. "Pard" Mustar, in their British-built Bristol Fighter. Australia's most decorated pilot, Smith was just one of more than 1,500 fighter "aces" produced by the battling nations during World War I. The war was also a spur to aircraft design. By its end, comparatively reliable machines with a range of 500 miles and a cruising speed of 100 miles per hour were commonplace.

The Players and the Planes

"They are all first class men and very keen."

AUSTRALIAN PRIME MINISTER
W. M. "BILLY" HUGHES

Early in 1919, Australia's Prime Minister, an irascible, rapier-witted Welshman named Billy Hughes, was in Paris attending peace talks. Some weeks before, Hughes had been approached by several Australian Flying Corps (AFC) airmen awaiting repatriation from England who had asked permission to fly their military planes back home to Australia. Aware of the publicity generated by Lord Northcliffe, who in 1913 had offered a £10,000 prize for the first nonstop transatlantic flight, the shrewd politician saw a priceless opportunity to raise Australia's international profile and, more important, to illustrate the role aeroplanes could play in the development of the sparsely settled and isolated southern continent.

Nowhere was the tyranny of distance more repressive than in Australia. Five million people lived around the southeastern coastal fringe of the three-million-square-mile continent, while the remainder was almost uninhabited. Away from the coast, there were virtually no roads or railways. For those settlers who had braved the isolation of the outback, illness or injury could mean a 1,000-mile ride for help. Even more daunting for some was Australia's distance from Britain, the "mother country", where many white Australians had strong family bonds. Britain was months away by sea.

On February 18, 1919, Hughes cabled his government back in Melbourne: *Several Australian aviators are desirous of attempting flight London–Australia in Handley Page machine. They are all first class men and very keen.* He suggested to his government colleagues in Melbourne that they should match Lord Northcliffe and offer a cash prize of £10,000 ($50,000) for the first crew to complete the mammoth, 11,250-mile flight from London to Darwin. Hughes explained: *It would be a great advertisement for Australia and would concentrate the eyes of the world on us.*

One month later, on March 19, the Australian government proclaimed: *With a view to stimulating aerial activity, the Commonwealth Government has decided to offer £10,000 for the first successful flight to Australia from Great Britain, in a machine manned by Australians.*

The rules for the "Great Trans-Planet Air Race" were drawn up by the Royal Aero Club in London. The race was controversial and was almost unanimously denounced by the press as a waste of money and, probably, lives. The early tragedies would add fuel to the fire, but Prime Minister Hughes stood firm and aggressively publicized the winners.

The announcement received a mixed reception in Australia. Several newspapers criticized the venture. The Melbourne *Age* described it as *a circus flight—a poorly disguised attempt at self-advertisement at the expense of the Australian public,* a reference to the fact that the prize would come out of taxpayers' money. The *Corowa Free Press* was even more scathing: *How many people care whether there is an aerial mail between Great Britain and Australia or not? They ought to carry on the experimental voyage as many Federal Members [Members of Australia's Parliament] as possible and leave them somewhere else.*

Nevertheless, plans went ahead, and at the request of the Australian government, Britain's Royal Aero Club drew up the rules. The competition was restricted to Australian airmen, and each crew could choose its own time to begin the flight. Once started, however, the flight had to be completed within thirty consecutive days—a tall order by the aviation standards of 1919! Apart from the demands this placed on the resilience of aircraft and crews, there were only a few, far-flung airfields scattered along the route. Spare parts and technical assistance would be virtually nonexistent at these remote strips.

Royal Aero Club of the United Kingdom,
3, CLIFFORD STREET, LONDON, W.1.

Telegraphic Address: "Aerodom, Reg. London."
Telephone: Regent 1327-8-9.

£10,000 PRIZE
Offered by the Australian Government for a Flight from Great Britain to Australia.
(Under the Competition Rules of the Royal Aero Club.)

The Australian Government have offered the sum of £10,000 to be awarded to the Pilot who shall first accomplish the flight in an aeroplane or seaplane from Great Britain to Australia in 720 consecutive hours.

The offer will remain open until midnight, the 31st December, 1920, by which date the flight must have been completed.

The complete aircraft and all its component parts must have been entirely constructed within the confines of the British Empire. Raw material may be obtained from other sources.

The Pilots and all crew must be of Australian Nationality, in accordance with the laws of the Australian Commonwealth.

Entries.—Entries are to be made to the Royal Aero Club, 3, Clifford Street, London, W.1. The Entry Form, which must be accompanied by the Entry Fee of £100, must be sent to the Secretary of the Club at least seven days before the start is made.
All entry fees received will be applied towards payment of the expenses of the Royal Aero Club in conducting the competition. Any balance not so expended will be refunded *pro rata* to the entrants.

Identification of Aircraft.—Only one aircraft may be used throughout the flight. Individual replacements and repairs to the aircraft and motors may be made *en route*, but neither may be changed as a whole. In the case of a seaplane, it may be taken ashore for such repairs and replacements. Five parts of the aircraft and five parts of each motor will be stamped or otherwise marked, and at least two marked parts of each of these five must be in place on arrival at the control and at the finishing point.

Starting Place.—The start must be made from Hounslow Aerodrome or Calshot Seaplane Station.
All starts must be made under the supervision of an official or officials appointed by the Royal Aero Club.

Finishing Place.—The point at which the competitor must finish in Australia will be in the neighbourhood of Port Darwin, and will be announced later.

Control.—A Control Station will be established on the route of the flight at Singapore. Competitors must alight at this control for purposes of identification.

Towing.—Towing on the water is not prohibited, but the total distance of such towing must not exceed 100 miles, of which not more than 50 miles shall be consecutive.

Timing.—The time of starting will be the time the aircraft leaves the ground or water, and the time of arrival will be deemed to be the time of crossing the coast line in the neighbourhood of Port Darwin.

GENERAL.

1. A competitor, by entering, thereby agrees that he is bound by the Regulations herein contained or to be hereafter issued in connection with this competition.

2. The interpretation of these regulations or of any to be hereafter issued shall rest entirely with the Royal Aero Club.

3. The competitor shall be solely responsible to the officials for the due observance of these regulations, and shall be the person with whom the officials will deal in respect thereof, or of any other question arising out of this competition.

4. A competitor, by entering, waives any right of action against the Royal Aero Club or the Australian Government for any damages sustained by him in consequence of any act or omission on the part of the officials of the Royal Aero Club or the Australian Government or their representatives or servants or any fellow competitor.

5. The aircraft shall at all times be at the risk in all respects of the competitor, who shall be deemed by entry to agree to waive all claim for injury either to himself, or his passenger, or his aircraft, or his employees or workmen, and to assume all liability for damage to third parties or their property, and to indemnify the Royal Aero Club and the Australian Government in respect thereof.

6. The Committee of the Royal Aero Club reserves to itself the right, with the consent of the Australian Government, to add to, amend or omit any of these rules should it think fit.

22nd May, 1919.   *For Entry Form, see over.*

GRIEF AND GALLANTRY

In Paris, French airman Jules Védrines was independently organizing a flight round the world. He had already written to Australian authorities requesting information on "landing grounds and flying conditions" over the great southern continent. Meanwhile, he made headlines—and earned 25,000 francs towards his proposed Australian trip—with a daring publicity stunt that involved landing an airplane on the flat roof of the Galeries Lafayette department store in the middle of Paris. But luck was about to run out for the daredevil Frenchman.

On April 21, 1919, Védrines took off from Paris with a photographer, bound for Rome on what appears to have been a warm-up for his Australian adventure. Shortly after he passed Lyon, one of his two engines failed. Unable to hold height, Védrines turned his crippled machine towards an open field, but crashed short in a vineyard. Both men were killed on impact, and all that remained of the plane was a tangled wreck. All France mourned the loss of the brave pilot, who had risen from the slums of Paris to become a national hero. He left a widow and four children.

The French challenge was prematurely over. Or so it seemed, until, on June 4, the French Foreign Office formally asked the Australian government whether a Frenchman could compete for the England–Australia prize. The request was made on behalf of former French Air Force pilot Étienne Poulet, a close friend of Védrines. On learning that his comrade's widow was destitute, Poulet determined to win the £10,000 prize—a fortune in those days—and present it to Madame Védrines in honor of her husband's memory. It was a bitter blow, therefore, when Poulet was told that the event was restricted to Australian airmen.

THE ATLANTIC CONQUERED

Ten days later, on June 14, former Royal Air Force airmen John Alcock and Arthur Whitten-Brown set out across the Atlantic in a Vickers Vimy bomber. Their nonstop flight of sixteen and a half hours in appalling conditions made world headlines: "Lords of the Air" trumpeted the London papers.

Étienne Poulet and his mechanic, Jean Benoist, set out for Australia in this war-surplus Caudron G.4 fighter bomber. Powered by 80-horsepower Le Rhône engines, it had a top speed of 80 miles per hour. During the war, as test pilot at the Caudron factory, Poulet flight-tested more than 1,400 airplanes, including numerous G.4s. He subsequently spent much of his life working in China, Vietnam and Cambodia as a flight instructor and aviation adviser to government.

Above: Jules Védrines was a hero of the long-distance races of 1911. Born in the slums of Paris, he had difficulty reading maps and kept getting lost. Nevertheless, he came fourth in the 1,000-mile Circuit of Europe and second in Lord Northcliffe's $50,000 Circuit of Britain. The lone finisher of the Paris–Madrid race, he was entertained by the King of Spain: such was the magnetism of the early aviators.

THE 1919 ATLANTIC CHALLENGE

"Yesterday I was in America…and I am the first man in Europe to say that."

JOHN ALCOCK, JUNE 15, 1919

I T WAS BRITISH newspaper magnate Alfred Harmsworth, the first Lord Northcliffe, who set the scene for adventure. An avid advocate of aviation, Northcliffe had sponsored several flying competitions before the war, and in 1913 had offered a staggering £10,000 ($50,000) prize for the first nonstop transatlantic flight. Several crews had been planning to make the 1,880-mile flight when World War I intervened.

In 1918, as the war ground to a close, Northcliffe's *Daily Mail* newspaper announced that the transatlantic prize was still up for grabs. Despite an initial rush, only five serious contestants eventually surfaced. Three were flying single-engine biplanes: Tom Sopwith's modified B.1 Atlantic, a Martinsyde Type A Mk. I and a Short Shirl. Of the other two, one was flying a twin-engine Vickers Vimy bomber, and the other, a giant, four-engine Handley Page 1500.

DOGGED BY MISFORTUNE

The Short was quickly out of contention when it ditched in the Irish Sea while attempting an east–west crossing in April 1919. The remaining competitors sailed to Newfoundland, only to be delayed by rain, snow and gales. The Martinsyde crashed on takeoff, injuring one of its crew. The Sopwith, flown by Harry

Above: British newspaper magnate Lord Northcliffe aroused European interest in flight. By sponsoring the 1909 cross-Channel challenge and the 1919 transatlantic affair, he helped bring about a new era in aviation.

Right: British pilot John Porte, here christening his twin-engine Curtiss flying boat *America* at Hammonds-port, New York, in 1914, was the first serious contender for Northcliffe's transatlantic challenge. The advanced design, which included an enclosed cabin, was financed by American department store tycoon Rodman Wanamaker. The outbreak of World War I precluded Porte's attempt, but Britain purchased fifty Curtiss planes for antisubmarine patrols.

Hawker, reached the middle of the Atlantic before being forced down by an overheating engine. Miraculously, Hawker and his navigator were rescued by a passing cargo ship, but as the ship had no radio, the rescue could not be reported to the anxious world. King George V offered condolences to Mrs. Hawker, and Lord Northcliffe gave her £5,000 ($25,000). She politely said she had yet to give up hope. Hawker set foot in Scotland the next day, and newspapers on both sides of the Atlantic frontpaged the amazing story. Vimy pilot John Alcock joked to his American-born navigator, Arthur Whitten-Brown: "Their hands are so blistered from clapping Harry Hawker that we'll be lucky to get a languid hand."

AN UNPROMISING START

On June 14, Alcock and Brown took off from a Newfoundland farm paddock. Loaded to the gills with 870 gallons of fuel and 40 gallons of

Alcock (left) was a fighter ace with seven "kills". Like Ross Smith, he flew Handley Page 0/400 bombers, but finished the war in a Turkish prison. There, he started planning the transatlantic flight. His navigator, Brown (right), seriously injured when shot down, spent two years as a prisoner of war. Alcock said: "My part was simple. The navigation was the ticklish part."

Below: For his takeoff from a tiny Newfoundland farm field, Alcock employed thirty locals to stand in front of the wings and hold back the fuel-laden Vimy as he ran the engines to full power. On Alcock's signal, the human brakes sat and ducked their heads as the plane shot forward.

Based on a Sopwith B.1 bomber, Hawker's *Atlantic* was modified to incorporate extra fuel tanks and an upturned dinghy built into the rear fuselage decking, behind the navigator's cockpit. Following takeoff, Hawker jettisoned the landing gear, which decreased the airplane's drag and increased its range. When an overheating engine forced Hawker down in the stormy mid-Atlantic, the absence of landing gear also helped him to ditch the Sopwith safely.

oil, their Vimy barely cleared rising ground at the end of the field. An hour later, Alcock had coaxed the biplane bomber to 1,500 feet, where it was sandwiched between cloud layers. Unable to take sextant readings, Brown navigated by dead reckoning.

The starboard engine's exhaust manifold blew away, adding a deafening roar to the slipstream noise of the open cockpit. Conversation was impossible, and the airmen communicated by gestures and written messages for the rest of the flight. During the night, they climbed above the main cloud bank, which allowed Brown to take his first worthwhile fix. The Vimy was slightly south of track and had a better than expected groundspeed of 122 miles per hour.

The flight almost came to an end toward sunrise, when they entered a bank of turbulent cloud. Brown wrote: *We lost our instinct of balance. The machine, left to its own devices, swung, flew amok, and began to perform circus tricks.* Completely disoriented, Alcock lost control, and the Vimy entered a violent spin. He throttled back but was unable to regain level flight. Preparing to crash, they suddenly broke out of the cloud, almost upside down, about 100 feet above the white-capped ocean.

During the long climb back through the clouds, sleet and snow built up a crust of ice on the Vimy. The instruments mounted on the engine cowlings became unreadable and the ailerons jammed, robbing Alcock of normal

Well-wishers move away from the icy slipstream as Fred Raynham, the twenty-year-old pilot of the Martinsyde, makes a final full-power check of his Rolls Royce Falcon engine. The airstrip was too short for the overloaded biplane. It had not gained sufficient speed when it mushed into the air, stalled and flopped back onto the ground. The landing gear collapsed, and the plane ended on its belly.

lateral control. Worse still, as a result of the carburettor intake icing up, the starboard engine lost power and started to backfire. Alcock had no option but to throttle back the ailing engine and descend to warmer air in the hope of melting the ice.

A VICTORY AGAINST THE ODDS

They were down to 1,000 feet before the ailerons freed, and to 500 feet when the Vimy broke out of the cloud. Alcock gingerly opened the throttle of the starboard engine and was rewarded by a surge of power. Twenty minutes later, they crossed the Irish coast and sighted the radio masts at Clifden. With six hours' fuel remaining, they could easily have reached London, but seeing the hills ahead shrouded in cloud, Alcock decided to play safe and land.

The flight of sixteen hours and twenty-eight minutes came to an end as Alcock brought the Vimy down on a lush green meadow at the edge of town. Too late, he recognized the tussocks of an Irish peat bog. The wheels touched down, and the biplane lurched to an inglorious stop in a spray of mud and water, tail-up and nose-down.

Awarding the airmen Lord Northcliffe's £10,000 check during a luncheon at London's Savoy Hotel, Winston Churchill quipped: "I don't really know what we should admire most in our guests: their audacity, their determination, their skill… or their good fortune."

Above: The Vimy nose-down in the bog at Clifden, in Ireland. Soldiers from a nearby camp thought the airmen were joking when they claimed to have flown the Atlantic. A small and very excited boy came splashing across the bog, and Alcock tossed him something from the cockpit. "Have an orange from America," he called.

Below: Alcock and Brown's Vickers Vimy is now displayed at London's Kensington Science Museum. Alcock crashed to his death in December 1919 while delivering a new Vickers Viking amphibian in fogbound France. Brown never flew again after the Atlantic affair.

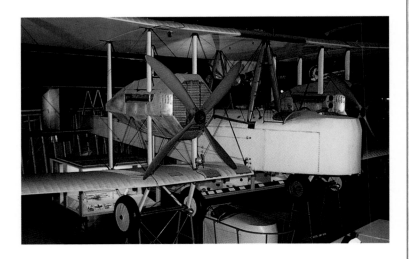

Lieutenant Valdemar Rendle, AFC, pictured here in bulky World War I flying gear, was the pilot of the Blackburn Kangaroo—a former antisubmarine patrol bomber. Rendle, who had finished the war as a ferry pilot delivering planes from England to the battle front in France, was flying a London–Paris mail run when he heard about the England–Australia challenge.

In New York, the *Times* reflected: *Like Alexander, the record-making aviator will soon weep because he has no more worlds to conquer.* As well as winning Lord Northcliffe's prize, Alcock and Brown were knighted for their valiant effort.

With the Atlantic affair over, attention focused on the England–Australia flight. Britain's Blackburn Aeroplane and Motor Company had already entered one of its Kangaroo bombers—so named for the pouchlike machine-gun housing slung under its body. The big, twin-engine biplane was to be piloted by Lieutenant Valdemar Rendle, AFC, the son of a Brisbane doctor. His crewmen were Lieutenant Cyril Maddocks and, as copilot, an airman who nine years later would conquer the Pacific, Lieutenant Charles Kingsford Smith.

The Fédération Aéronautique Internationale (the world governing body) and the Royal Aero Club judged that the Kangaroo's crew had insufficient navigational experience to safely guide the aircraft to Australia—an ironic decision viewed in light of Kingsford Smith's later pioneering flights. Lieutenant Rendle's Blackburn Kangaroo was finally accepted following the nomination of Captain Hubert Wilkins as navigator. Wilkins brought to the crew a wealth of navigational and meteorological expertise gained as a member of Vilhjalmur Steffansson's 1914 polar expedition. By this time, Kingsford Smith and Maddocks had withdrawn from the team, and their places had been taken by Lieutenants Reg Williams and Garnsey St. Clair Potts.

OTHER CONTENDERS

The Alliance Aeroplane Co. Ltd. had provided Lieutenants Roger M. Douglas and James L. Ross with a big P.2 Seabird biplane equipped with a 450-horsepower Napier Lion engine. Christened *Endeavour*, the aircraft sported an unusual enclosed, and quite lavish, cabin with upholstered leather seats. It even had a two-way radio—a rarity in those days. Originally designed with the transatlantic crossing in mind, but completed too late, the Alliance's 515-gallon fuel tank gave it a massive, 2,000-mile range at a cruising speed of 100 miles per hour. A former army machine gunner twice decorated for bravery, Lieutenant Douglas transferred to the AFC in 1918 and became a flight instructor. His navigator–radio operator, Ross, had served as a ferry pilot before he was posted to No. 2 Squadron, AFC, in France, where he was seriously wounded during a dogfight.

The Sopwith Aviation Company entered a Wallaby biplane similar to a machine flown by Tom Sopwith's Australian test pilot, Harry Hawker, in Lord Northcliffe's transatlantic challenge. Sopwith nominated Captain George Matthews as pilot and Sergeant Thomas Kay as flight mechanic and assistant pilot. A former ship's master and navigator, Matthews had served at Gallipoli with the Australian Light Horse before transferring to the AFC. Following a stint flying fighter planes, he became a flight instructor specializing in aerial navigation. Kay, who had served as a mechanic with the AFC, qualified for his pilot's licence in 1919 while working with Rolls Royce Ltd. in England.

Lieutenants Roger Douglas (pilot) and James Ross (navigator–radio operator), AFC, pose with their Alliance P.2 Seabird, *Endeavour*, at Hounslow on November 13, 1919. Minutes after takeoff, the Seabird spun into the ground, killing both airmen. Following a coroner's finding of accidental death, Ross's distraught fiancée alleged a coverup. She claimed that the plane had not been properly flight-tested following repairs resulting from an earlier crash. A subsequent Committee of Inquiry found that the airmen had inadvertently entered a spin at insufficient altitude to recover.

Below: The *Endeavour* was one of a pair of P.2s built to take part in the 1919 transatlantic competition. They were completed too late, but one, G-EAGL, made the first nonstop flight between London and Madrid on July 31, 1919. Powered by a 450-horsepower Napier Lion engine, the lavishly equipped cabin biplane had a top speed of 140 miles per hour.

Like Sopwith Aviation, the Martinsyde Company was keen to erase the memory of a failed Atlantic contender. It entered a Type A Mk. 1 biplane powered by a 275-horsepower Rolls Royce Falcon engine. Fighter ace Captain Cedric Howell was chosen as pilot, with Air Mechanic George Fraser as crewman. Three times decorated for gallantry, Captain Howell began his military career as an Australian Army sniper. Late in the war, he had transferred to the Royal Air Force, where his marksman's eye helped him become an ace fighter pilot. In the course of flying Sopwith Camels over the Western Front, he was credited with shooting down nineteen enemy aircraft. Fraser, who had served with No. 1 Bombing Squadron, AFC, took a special course in aerial navigation to meet the England–Australia entry requirements. At the age of forty, he was the oldest contestant, most of the crews being in their early twenties.

THE RACE FAVORITE

A last-minute entry was the Vickers Vimy F.B.27A, which had been the backup machine for Alcock and Brown's transatlantic flight. Its crew were brothers Captain Ross Macpherson Smith and Lieutenant Keith Macpherson Smith, together with flight mechanics Sergeants Walter Shiers and James Bennett. The Vimy appeared an obvious favorite to take out the prize. Not only had the aircraft proved its reliability and strength during the Atlantic crossing, but its crew were the best qualified—Ross Smith in particular, who had experience of much of the route to Australia.

Ross Smith was no stranger to adventure. From March 1917, when he qualified as a pilot, until the war's end, he had flown in the Middle East. Besides flying Bristol Fighters, he was personal pilot to the legendary Lawrence of Arabia. As Australia's most-decorated airman—with six medals for gallantry—Ross Smith's escapades were the stuff of Errol Flynn movies. Nicknamed "Hadji", he was credited with nine kills. Once, when a German plane appeared overhead during his breakfast, Hadji took his meal aloft and, when he ran out of ammunition, threw his plate of breakfast

Left: Captain George Matthews, AFC (*top*), the pilot of the Sopwith Aviation Company's Wallaby biplane, and (*below*) his assistant pilot and flight mechanic, Sergeant Thomas Kay, AFC.

The Martinsyde Type A Mk. I was powered by a 275-horsepower Rolls Royce Falcon engine and had a range of 1,200 miles. Its predecessor crashed on takeoff during the 1919 transatlantic competition.

Before taking off for Australia from Hounslow, near London, on November 12, 1919, the Vimy crew posed with Vickers officials on the snowbound airfield. In flying clothing, from left to right: Ross Smith, Keith Smith, James Bennett and Walter Shiers. The tall man (fifth from the right) is Rex Pierson, the designer of the Vickers Vimy.

A LETTER FROM THE FRONT

Patriotism is a wonderful thing, isn't it? Here are hundreds of men as happy as kings because they are going to face bullets, and I bet that half of them couldn't tell you what started this war. But it's that wonderful British fighting spirit in them that is crying out for adventure and danger more than anything else.

ROSS SMITH IN A LETTER WRITTEN TO HIS MOTHER FROM HELIOPOLIS ON THE NIGHT BEFORE THE AUSTRALIAN THIRD LIGHT HORSE LEFT EGYPT FOR TURKEY, MAY 17, 1915

sausages at the enemy. Recounting details of aerial engagements in his book *The Seven Pillars of Wisdom*, T. E. Lawrence wrote: *Ross Smith wished he might stay forever on this Arab front with an enemy [aircraft coming over] every half hour.* Late in the war, Ross Smith commanded a big Handley Page 0/400 bomber on missions over Turkey.

Ross Smith had sought desperately to be the first man to fly to Australia when the war ended. He made an attempt in the Handley Page late in 1918, which started in Cairo and got as far as Calcutta. From India, Smith and his British copilot, Brigadier General A. E. Borton, together with their mechanics, Sergeants Wally Shiers and Jim Bennett, boarded a steamer, RIMS *Sphinx*, in an effort to survey possible landing sites along the 5,000-mile route between Calcutta and Darwin, Australia—over which no airplane had ever flown. The *Sphinx* exploded and immediately sank in Chittagong harbor. The airmen escaped with only their lives. They completed the survey through to Timor, in the Dutch East Indies (now Indonesia), aboard RIMS *Minto*, despite a few bouts of malaria.

Upon returning to India, Smith and his mechanics were devastated when they learned that their plane, the only one in that part of the world, had been commandeered by the British Army to help suppress an Afghan uprising and destroyed in a storm. Their efforts over the seven months up to June 1919 had been for nought—or so they had thought until now.

A sixth entry had been received from Lieutenant Raymond Parer, AFC, who had flown in Europe during the war as a test and delivery pilot. Parer was still negotiating with the Beardmore Aero Company, but appeared an unlikely contender.

THE QUIXOTIC FRENCHMAN

By the middle of October, when the crews were busy with their final preparations, startling news came from across the Channel. Étienne Poulet, the loyal friend of Jules Védrines, had made a gallant, if somewhat quixotic, gesture. Withdrawing his life savings and borrowing from friends, he scraped together just enough cash to buy a war-surplus Caudron G.4 biplane and to cover flight expenses. As well as bringing glory to France, Poulet intended to give fund-raising displays and exhibitions during the journey to Australia. The proceeds would go to Madame Védrines. The lightweight G.4 had earned a reputation as one of the most efficient planes of its day. Powered by a pair of tiny, 80-horsepower Le Rhône rotary engines, it weighed a mere 3,170 pounds fully loaded.

Before setting off from Villacoublay, near Paris, on October 14, Poulet explained to the press: "I was Védrines' friend. He planned to make this flight. Death prevented Védrines. I will replace him. *Voila tout.* If I arrive, perhaps I may win the big Australian prize. Perhaps!" His flight mechanic, Jean Benoist, chimed in: "It would be for Védrines' children. They need it badly."

THE LONG REACH TO AUSTRALIA

"… I am a silly ass for having ever
embarked on the flight."

CAPTAIN ROSS SMITH

The Sopwith Wallaby was the first away in what journalists were already calling "the Trans-Planet Air Race". At 8:30 a.m. on October 21, Matthews and Kay arrived at a fog-shrouded Hounslow Aerodrome to find Sopwith mechanics busy tuning the Wallaby's engine. A group of journalists hung around, keeping an eye on a notice board that announced: "Machine: Sopwith—Destination: Australia—Starting Time: When Fog Clears."

Seeing the airmen approach the Wallaby, they rushed over to get pictures and interviews. Asked if he was confident of reaching Australia, Matthews replied: "No, but I am hopeful. It is impossible to be confident in the face of such a task, but I am satisfied that nobody could have a better machine for the attempt." Mechanic Kay shrewdly added: "The human factor is reliable. The unknown quantity is the engine's power of endurance under varying [climatic] conditions. The conditions of this flight are such that a preliminary test was impossible."

The pair loaded their in-flight rations (chocolate, tinned food and flasks of hot cocoa) and then pulled fur-lined leather flying suits over their Australian Flying Corps uniforms. Watching their preparations, an eagle-eyed reporter asked why the Sopwith was not equipped with a collapsible boat. "That would merely prolong the agony," replied Matthews.

By mid-morning, the fog had lifted, and the Wallaby took off, climbing slowly south toward the English Channel. Striking thick fog over the French coast, Matthews and Kay were forced to land at Marquise, only a few miles inland from Calais, where they were obliged to wait two days for the fog to clear. The two airmen reached Cologne on the afternoon of October 23, but were again delayed by bad weather. This time, they had to wait ten days. Europe was in the grip of a bitter winter. Snow, sleet, rain and fog were to keep the two frustrated Australians grounded for days on end. By mid-November, the Wallaby team was still snowbound in Germany.

GOD 'ELP ALL OF US

Back in England, Ross Smith and his crew moved to Weybridge to be close to the Vickers factory, which was located in the middle of the famous Brooklands motor-racing track. There was much to be done. The modifications that had to be made to the Vimy for the flight included removing the gun mounts, increasing the fuel capacity to 516 gallons, strengthening the fuselage, and installing a shock absorber on the control column to remove the load from the pilot's shoulder and back. There

Rugged up in a borrowed fur coat, Captain George Matthews, AFC, inspects the Sopwith Wallaby in its hangar at Dagsburg, in Alsace Lorraine. Although the Wallaby's crew took off three weeks ahead of the Vimy, their decision to take a more northerly route across Europe cost them any chance of being the first to Australia. Becoming snowbound during the severe winter, they lost almost two months.

Snow in November is virtually unknown in southern England. But on November 12, 1919, snow settled as the Vimy G-EAOU was prepared for flight at Hounslow Aerodrome, just 2 miles from today's London airport at Heathrow. The weather forecast was Class V, totally unfit for flying, but as Ross Smith recalled, *[O]ur minds were made up and, come fair, come foul, we were determined to start.*

was no trimming system, as in modern aircraft, which allows pilots to fly "hands-off".

Weight was a critical problem. Recounting his story for the *National Geographic* magazine in 1921, Ross Smith wrote: *We discovered that, after the "weighing in", there was an excess of 300 pounds; so something had to go. Our "spares" were indispensable, and so we drastically attacked our personal kit…and so it eventuated that we left England in the garments we wore and with the proverbial tooth-brush apiece.*

For convenience, Ross Smith had broken up the route and its twenty-four planned refueling stops into four sectors: London to Cairo; Cairo to Calcutta; Calcutta to Singapore; and Singapore to Darwin. Time was allowed at the end of each stage for the Vimy to be given a thorough checkover. Before the Vimy was officially handed over to its Australian crew, it was flight-tested by Vickers pilot Sir John Alcock, fresh from his Atlantic triumph. The Vimy's registration marking was the letters G-EAOU—which the crew joked stood for "God 'Elp All Of Us".

COME FAIR, COME FOUL

The formalities now over, Ross Smith and his crew waited for a break in the weather to make the fifteen-minute flight from the Vickers factory at Brooklands to Hounslow, the official starting place for all entrants. Ross Smith wrote: *The weather during this week's stay was abominable. Winter was fast closing in with typical English November fogs. Driving sleet and pelting rains fell almost without intermission. One afternoon there was a brief lull, and I managed to get the machine into the air for about an hour and make a final test….On November 11 we were pottering around our machine when the rain suddenly ceased and the fog lifted. It was too good an opportunity to miss!*

Above: Powered by two 360-horsepower Rolls Royce engines, the Vickers Vimy had a maximum speed of 103 miles per hour and a range of 1,040 miles. Impressed by its performance and reliability, Ross Smith wrote in 1921 that the Vimy *inspired in me great confidence and opened my eyes to the possibilities of modern aëroplanes and their application to commercial uses.*

Below: A handwritten note from the secretary of the Royal Aero Club confirming Captain Ross Smith's entry as a contestant in the England–Australia race. The letter mentions the mechanics Walter Shiers and James Bennett but not Keith Smith, who had just been released from service with the Royal Air Force (RAF).

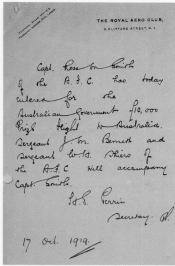

The pocket compass carried by Vimy mechanic Wally Shiers would have been of little use in flight. It would have been affected by vibration and by magnetic errors induced by the engines on either side of the mechanics' open cockpit.

The decision had been taken. On November 12, the Vimy crew were up at 4:30 a.m. It was a clear and frosty day. The machine was run out from the hangar, and officials marked and sealed five aircraft parts. Competition rules required that the crew produce at least three marked parts on arrival in Australia to prove that they had not changed aircraft en route. By 8 a.m., despite the airfield being covered in snow and once again shrouded in fog, Ross and Keith Smith took off for Australia. Ross Smith wrote: *[O]ur minds were made up and, come fair, come foul, we were determined to start.*

As the big bomber lifted slowly from the field, the crew very nearly came to grief. With Ross Smith's permission, a zealous photographer had positioned his camera and tripod about 300 yards along their takeoff run. In the mud and snow, the heavily laden aircraft took longer than expected to get airborne. Seconds after liftoff, the Vimy clipped the camera as the alarmed photographer dived for safety. The camera must have come in contact with either the nose or the tailskid, for the Vimy was undamaged. Air Mechanic Wally Shiers recalled: *We heard this*

crash, bang, rattle. We looked out and couldn't see nothing. Anyhow, she got in the air and was flying along all right.

The Vimy left England as the firm race favorite. Built for long-range bombing missions over Germany, with two 360-horsepower Rolls Royce Eagle VIII engines, the giant biplane had a maximum speed of 103 miles per hour. With its additional fuel tanks, G-EAOU had a maximum range of 1,040 miles. Besides being a well-trained and closely knit team, the crew were superbly fit following a special course of intensive physical training. The four men were seated in two open cockpits, with the pilot and navigator in the middle cockpit, behind the nose gunner's seat, and the mechanics in the rear cockpit, where they could keep an eye on the engines. Flight instruments in the open pilot's cockpit gave only airspeed, altitude and direction, and there was no radio. Overland navigation was done by map, and over water they flew by a combination of compass, clock, speed and pure "gut feeling".

Crossing the English coast at Folkestone, the crew were in high spirits. Ross Smith wrote eloquently: *[T]here is something more majestic and stable about the big bombers which a pilot begins to love. An exquisite community grows up between machine and pilot; each, as it were, merges into the other. The machine is*

The cockpit of the Vickers Vimy G-EAOU reflects aviation's "seat-of-the-pants" era, when night or cloud flying was risky business. The primitive flight instruments gave only altitude, airspeed and direction. Navigation was done by map, clock and compass. Several of G-EAOU's instruments were souvenired following the England–Australia flight.

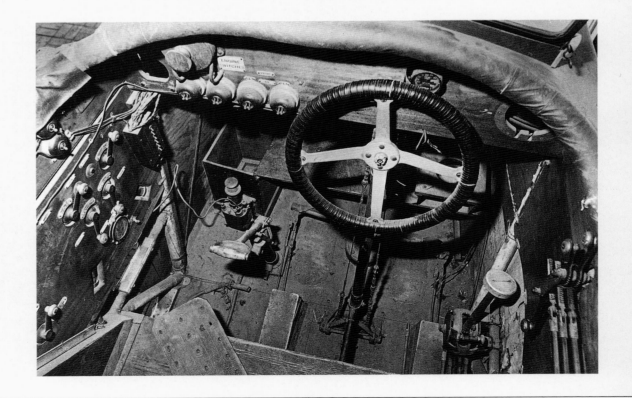

rudimentary and the pilot the intellectual force. The levers and controls are the nervous system of the machine, through which the will of the pilot may be expressed—and expressed to an infinitely fine degree. A flying-machine is something entirely apart from and above all other contrivances of man's ingenuity. The aëroplane is the nearest thing to animate life that man has created.

FLYING BLIND

The moment they crossed the French coast, the weather changed, and they were confronted by, as Ross Smith described it, *a sea of cloud*. The flight to Lyon, in central France, became a nightmare. Unable to climb above the clouds, the Vimy's absolute ceiling being only 10,500 feet, they plunged through, thinking it might be only a narrow belt of coastal cloud. Blinding snow and sleet drove into the open cockpits. To the numbed airmen, it was like a polar blizzard as the aircraft's forward speed whipped the precipitation into the unprotected parts of their faces. The windshield iced over, their goggles clogged up with snow, and their faces became icy masks.

The brothers took turns peering ahead, looking for a break in the weather. Each could manage only a few minutes with his face bared to the lacerating fury of the weather before he had to duck low in the cockpit to thaw out while the other took his place. For a short while, they broke clear of the cloud by climbing to 8,000 feet. Although this freed them from the snow, the higher altitude exposed them to even more bitter cold. Even their sandwiches froze solid. In his log, Ross recorded: *This sort of flying is a rotten game. The cold is hell, and I am a silly ass for having ever embarked on the flight.*

The crew's only comfort came from the engines, which never missed a beat. As Ross Smith put it, *They roared away and sang a deep-throated song, filled with contentment and gladness…* His limbs almost lifeless from the cold, he was envious of the engines' warmth. *It seemed anomalous, too, that those engines needed water flowing around their cylinders to keep them cool, while we were sitting just a few feet away semi-frozen.*

Thirty-eight miles from their destination, they eventually managed to break out of the storm by spiraling down through a small gap in the clouds. After an exhausting flight lasting six hours and twenty minutes, they landed at Lyon, having flown 510 miles on a day officially reported as "unfit for all flying". Ross Smith would later recall that the first day's flying was the worst part of the entire England–Australia flight.

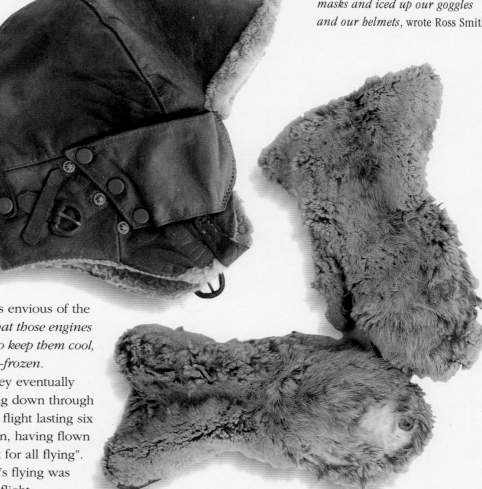

Helmet, goggles and gloves were icons of the open-cockpit years of aviation. Despite extensive use of fur on Keith Smith's leather helmet, goggles and flying gauntlets (shown here), he and the other Vimy crew members suffered terribly from the cold while crossing Europe. *Our hands and feet lost all feeling and our bodies became well-nigh frozen. The icy wind penetrated our thick clothing and it was with greatest difficulty that I could work the machine. Our breaths condensed on our faces and face-masks and iced up our goggles and our helmets*, wrote Ross Smith.

THE GRIM REALITY

The next morning, November 13, only an hour after the Vimy departed Lyon for Pisa, Lieutenants Roger Douglas and James Ross were busy preparing to leave Hounslow in the *Endeavour*. The two AFC pilots had intended to set off two weeks earlier, but had seriously damaged their aircraft when landing after their final test flight. The mishap had been hushed up, and few people—certainly not the press—were aware that a wing, part of the fuselage and the landing gear had had to be rebuilt.

On the morning they took off for Australia, the two airmen climbed into their seats and looked around at their comfortable quarters, crammed with equipment: dual controls, five days' rations, medical supplies, tea, coffee, water, special navigation charts, spare flying suits, and revolvers. It seemed the designers had thought of everything. Earlier, Douglas had told the press: "Only a mishap, such as is sometimes unavoidable with the best machine and organization, will prevent us landing in Australia. After all, it is pioneering, with the usual pioneering difficulties, but we are splendidly backed and have left nothing to chance."

Shortly before takeoff, they were handed several farewell messages, including one from General Sir W. R. Birdwood, Commanding Officer of the Australian Imperial Force (AIF). It said, in part: *You know all the difficulties and dangers of the route, but you are no more daunted by these than your brother officers were by the perils of war. Go on boys, win over the forces of air and space. It is such men who have made the British Empire.*

At 11:33 a.m. precisely, the Alliance's engine was started. "I expect to overtake the Vimy tomorrow," Douglas told reporters. It was no idle boast. As well as being slightly faster than the Vimy, the Alliance was smaller and had a single engine. This enabled it to travel 2,000 miles on its 515-gallon fuel load, giving it almost twice the range of the big, twin-engine Vimy. With this huge range advantage, Douglas and Ross planned to fly nonstop to Brindisi, in southern Italy, leapfrogging the Vimy, the snowbound Sopwith and the bad weather alike.

As the Alliance took off, Douglas and Ross waved to the crowd from the windows of their luxurious cabin. They circled the field, climbing slowly to an altitude of 1,200 feet, as recorded in the plane's log book, and then set on course for Australia.

Departing Hounslow a day after the Vimy, Douglas and Ross were confident of overtaking the Smith brothers. Having twice the Vimy's range, the Alliance would require fewer time-consuming refueling stops. The location of the pilot's cabin, tucked behind the massive fuselage fuel tank, was far from ideal and may have been a factor in Douglas's fatal loss of control.

Damascus, photographed by Ross Smith on November 19, 1919. Describing the crew's arrival in the city for *National Geographic* magazine in 1921, Ross Smith wrote lyrically: *...Damascus, a miraged streak on the horizon of a desert wilderness. The streak became irregular. It grew into a band assuming height and breadth... Color crept in; details resolved, developed, enlarged; a city arose from out of the waste of sands, an oasis, glorious, magical, enchanting—this was Damascus. A city almost ethereal in its beauty, rearing a forest of slender minarets and cupolas...*

The Vimy stood on a high and relatively drier part of the airfield, but the moment it started to roll forward, it again became bogged to its axles. In desperation, Ross Smith revved the engines, but was forced to cut the power when he felt the tail lift and the machine start to nose over. To overcome this problem, Bennett jumped down from his cockpit and threw his weight on the tailplane while the pilot revved the engines once again. Slowly at first, and then with gathering momentum, the Vimy moved forward through the mud, and Bennett was forced to run alongside, to be hauled aboard at the last minute by Wally Shiers. *I am sure that in a cinema picture our performance would resemble the take-off of a seaplane more than that of a land machine rising from an aërodrome,* Ross Smith wrote. As it turned out, he and his crew got off (and Bennett got on) just in time.

The Australians crossed the Mediterranean safely and followed the barren desert coastline until they saw the lush green ribbon of land fringing the Nile. Happy to be back on his old stomping ground, Ross Smith recalled: *Now we were winging our way over Old Father Nile and across landmarks that were as familiar to me as the Heliopolis aërodrome itself, to which destination I was guiding the Vimy.*

WRIGLEY'S TO THE RESCUE

They landed in Cairo after a flight lasting seven and a half hours. The European stage of the flight was over, and they were back on schedule. At Heliopolis, skilled RAF mechanics gave the Vickers a thorough checkover in preparation for the heat and sand of the Middle East leg. There was already one mechanical fault to fix. One of the Vimy's engines had been overheating on the run to Cairo, and Shiers quickly located the problem: a cracked induction pipe. The Australian airmen and their hosts unsuccessfully searched all the other airfields around Cairo and Alexandria for a replacement. A telegram to Vickers in London brought the reply that it would take two weeks to ship the part by sea.

A desperate situation called for desperate measures, and it was the inventive Shiers who came up with the answer. Fetching the Vimy's supply of Wrigley's chewing gum, he asked his bemused companions to start chewing. When a large ball of gum had been accumulated, Shiers spread the sticky mass around the fractured pipe, covered the putty-like poultice with a bandage of electrician's friction tape, and then sealed the bulging joint with several coats of shellac. A dubious Ross Smith inspected the makeshift repair. Turning to the grinning mechanic, he said: "We'll take her up for an air test." Miraculously, the repair held, and the temperature of the offending Eagle motor returned to normal.

SOJOURN IN THE DESERT

They left for Damascus the next morning, November 19, and refueled there for the long desert crossing to Baghdad. The following day, as the Vimy droned over an endless sea of sand,

Minutes later, the biplane emerged below the clouds. It went into a spin, recovered momentarily, but then entered, in the words of a horrified eyewitness, "a further clocklike spin and crashed to the earth". The Alliance smashed into a large apple tree. Ross was thrown out of the cabin roof and killed instantly; Douglas survived for a few minutes after being pulled from the wreckage but never regained consciousness. Their dream of flying home had ended in an apple orchard just 6 miles from Hounslow Aerodrome.

UP TO THE AXLES IN MUD

The Vimy, meanwhile, had been bogged while trying to take off in pouring rain from Pisa's waterlogged airfield. Thirty Italian mechanics toiled for nearly two hours to extricate the aircraft from the sticky morass, only to see it again become bogged during the second attempt at takeoff. By the following morning, November 15, conditions had not improved. It was still raining, and parts of the airfield were under water. Fearing that they might be grounded for days, Ross Smith decided to attempt a takeoff. The crew had heard that Poulet was nearing India, and every day wasted lessened their chance of catching the redoubtable Frenchman.

the pilots had to contend with a brisk headwind, and soon realized that they would not make Baghdad by nightfall. Lacking the proper equipment to fly at night, they decided to make an unscheduled stop at Ramadi, half an hour short of their destination.

The British regiment of the 10th Indian Lancers was based in the little desert town at the time, and they gave the airmen a warm welcome. The exhausted Australians had hoped for a good night's sleep, but around midnight, the wind that had frustrated them all day rose to gale force. The crew rushed to the airfield to find the Vimy straining against her tie-down

ropes and in danger of breaking free. With the help of fifty soldiers, they spent the night fighting to prevent their aircraft from being wrecked. At dawn, the wind dropped as suddenly as it had blown up. In dead calm, they topped up the fuel tanks and took off, bypassing Baghdad and landing instead, three and a half hours later, at Basra, on November 21.

THE EMBATTLED KANGAROO
Back in England, Captain Hubert Wilkins and Lieutenant Valdemar Rendle and their crew had at last set off in pursuit of the Smith brothers. Their Blackburn Kangaroo was no faster

This rugged mountain country was photographed by Ross Smith as the Vimy skirted the Persian Gulf near Bushire (Iran). Concerned at their complete isolation from civilization, Ross Smith wrote: *Throughout this terrible country I scarcely observed a possible landing ground, and had our engines failed us it would have meant either crashing or else an immersion in the Persian Gulf.*

than the Vimy, so their hopes were pinned on the chance that the Smith brothers would strike trouble on the "horror stretch" across the Middle East and India. Failing that, the Vimy might well be delayed by mechanical problems or monsoonal storms between India and Darwin.

For a week the Kangaroo battled its way across Europe, plagued by winds, rain and snow as winter set in. At one stage, when a 40-mile-per-hour headwind slashed their groundspeed by half, they watched despondently as their sluggish aircraft was overtaken by cars on the road below. As assistant pilot Williams later recounted, "Potts asked to be allowed to get out and walk."

Forced landings cost the Kangaroo yet more precious time. Following an overnight stop in France, the aircraft had developed ignition problems. Sir Hubert Wilkins recalled: *We came down in still another forced landing, examined the engine, and found one of the ignition wires had been disconnected and bound with soft wire to the frame of the aeroplane. Someone had deliberately tampered with the machine hoping to wreck us.* This was not to be the only time the Kangaroo's crew suspected sabotage of their bid for victory.

By December 5, the Kangaroo was through the bad weather and making excellent time down the coast of Greece en route to Crete. Although the airfield at Suda (now Soúda) Bay was sticky from recent heavy rains, the plane landed without incident. But the next morning, there were real problems. Overnight, the heavily loaded biplane had sunk into the black quagmire and was thoroughly bogged.

The task of digging it out fell to a group of a hundred Bulgarian prisoners of war still being held on the island. Three days later, when conditions seemed to have improved sufficiently to attempt a takeoff, the lumbering great bomber once again became bogged. The frustrated crew returned to their hotel to wait for the airfield to dry out properly.

THE MYSTERIOUS FATE OF THE MARTINSYDE

Meanwhile, on the morning of December 4, fighter ace Captain Cedric Howell and mechanic George Fraser had left England in the Martinsyde. Shouting "Ta-ta boys. We're

off!" to a small crowd gathered at Hounslow, they taxied away from the hangar and took off quickly, with a minimum of fuss. Howell had married while in England, and his wife was already bound for Australia in the liner *Orsova* as the airmen set off from Hounslow. He hoped to overtake the ship near Naples and, as a romantic gesture, to circle it.

Like the competitors ahead of them, Howell and Fraser encountered atrocious flying conditions over France and northern Italy, almost colliding with trees on the first day as they threaded their way through a cloud-capped valley. "The valley ended in a mountain ridge, so we just climbed up into the clouds and trusted to luck," Howell told journalists that night as they rested at Dijon. Next day, en route to Pisa, Italy, they were forced down by gales at Toulon.

Their luck ran out on December 9 between Taranto and Athens. Eight hours after takeoff, the Martinsyde was seen flying in semidarkness over St. George's Bay on the island of Corfu. Minutes later, it came down in the sea, only a few hundred yards from the shore. It seems that Howell managed to make a safe ditching, as peasants on the shore reported hearing cries for help. But the sea was too rough to launch a boat, and by the time conditions had moderated, the biplane had sunk in 12 feet of water. Howell's body was washed ashore, but no trace was ever found of Fraser.

What happened to the Martinsyde in the eight hours after it left Taranto remains a mystery to this day. With a cruising speed of 100 miles per hour, the plane should have made Athens in four hours. The island of Corfu, on the other hand, was only ninety minutes' flying time from their takeoff point. Perhaps the airmen got lost in the misty rain that plagued their route and flew around for eight hours trying to find their way.

It was also suggested that they may have landed in some remote field and waited out the bad weather, only to take off and strike further difficulties. Whether Howell was forced down by empty fuel tanks, mechanical problems or sheer fatigue, there seems little doubt that he was drawn by the lights of the nearby township. In the darkness and drizzle, it is unlikely the airmen realized that the sea would be so rough as to prevent their rescue.

In Pursuit of Poulet

By December 9, the England–Australia challenge had cost four lives and three of the five competing aircraft. The tragic crash of the Alliance, the tribulations of the Blackburn Kangaroo, and now the tragedy of the Martinsyde, had tended to divert public attention from the race-leading Vickers Vimy. During the last two weeks, the Smith brothers had been steadily closing the gap on the French pilot, Poulet.

On November 23, the Vimy made an uneventful flight from Basra to Bandar Abbas (in modern-day Iran). Ahead lay the 777-mile "horror stretch" to Karachi. This was the part of the flight that every airman feared most. It was over one of the world's most savage landscapes: hour after hour of jagged mountains interspersed with patches of white-hot desert. A forced landing in such terrain meant certain death. Ross Smith later recalled his feelings at the prospect: *The distance did not perturb me in the least, but the treacherous country and the isolation from civilization in case of a forced landing,* *and another long stretch of detestable mountain-scored country was in itself enough to give one a nightmare. The British Consul had prepared an ostentatious-looking document which we were to carry. It commanded the murderous tribes which infested the country to treat us kindly, in case we were compelled to land among them!* Fortunately, they never needed the documents, commonly known as "ghoolie chits" in those days.

Two weeks earlier, on November 10, Poulet and Benoist had been attacked by armed brigands after a forced landing at Pussni (now Pasni), close to the Gulf of Oman. Fortunately, the tribesmen were not carrying firearms and quickly dispersed when the Frenchmen fired warning pistol shots. For two days, the stranded airmen worked on an ailing engine, taking turns to stand guard at night. On the second night, they were attacked twice and a flaming torch was thrown at their aircraft. It is doubtful they got much sleep. The following day, November 12, as the Vimy was leaving England in hot pursuit, the Frenchmen managed to get their plane back in the air and head for Karachi.

Before clambering down from the Vimy cockpit at Bandar Abbas, Ross Smith photographed the welcoming committee headed by the Persian Governor (leaning on his walking stick) and the British Consul (in white). Here, the British Consul handed the airmen an "ostentatious-looking document" to carry with them on the leg to Karachi (then India)—a region where most tribesmen did not take kindly to British colonial rule. Ross Smith recalled: *It commanded the murderous tribes which infested the country to treat us kindly, in case we were compelled to land among them!*

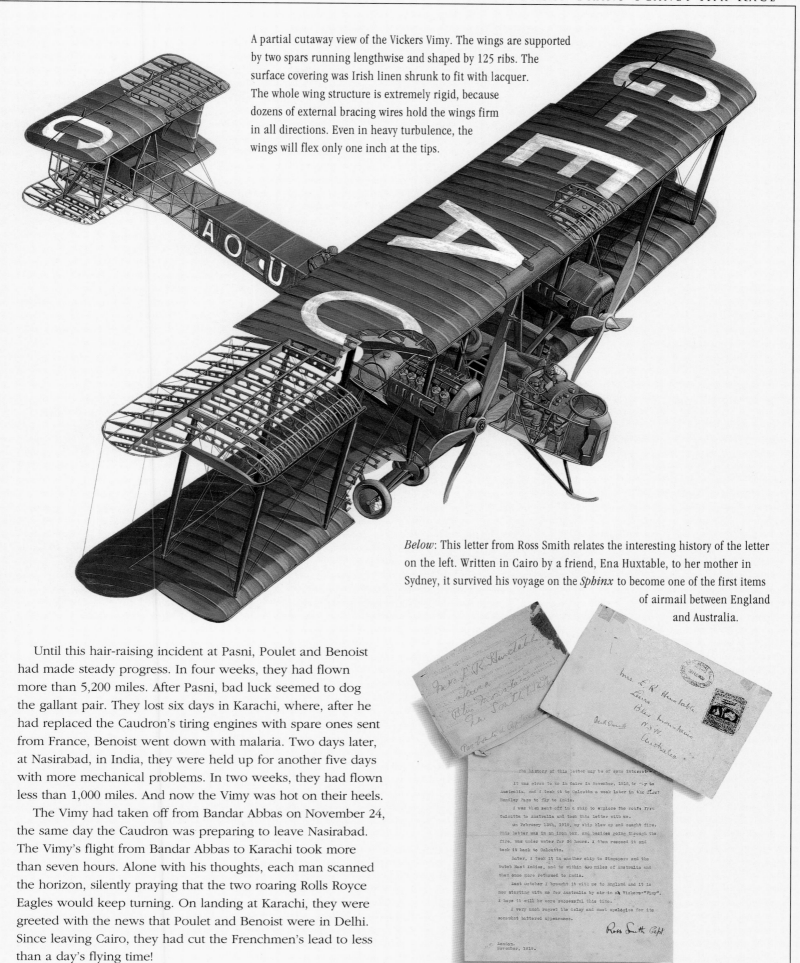

A partial cutaway view of the Vickers Vimy. The wings are supported by two spars running lengthwise and shaped by 125 ribs. The surface covering was Irish linen shrunk to fit with lacquer. The whole wing structure is extremely rigid, because dozens of external bracing wires hold the wings firm in all directions. Even in heavy turbulence, the wings will flex only one inch at the tips.

Below: This letter from Ross Smith relates the interesting history of the letter on the left. Written in Cairo by a friend, Ena Huxtable, to her mother in Sydney, it survived his voyage on the *Sphinx* to become one of the first items of airmail between England and Australia.

Until this hair-raising incident at Pasni, Poulet and Benoist had made steady progress. In four weeks, they had flown more than 5,200 miles. After Pasni, bad luck seemed to dog the gallant pair. They lost six days in Karachi, where, after he had replaced the Caudron's tiring engines with spare ones sent from France, Benoist went down with malaria. Two days later, at Nasirabad, in India, they were held up for another five days with more mechanical problems. In two weeks, they had flown less than 1,000 miles. And now the Vimy was hot on their heels.

The Vimy had taken off from Bandar Abbas on November 24, the same day the Caudron was preparing to leave Nasirabad. The Vimy's flight from Bandar Abbas to Karachi took more than seven hours. Alone with his thoughts, each man scanned the horizon, silently praying that the two roaring Rolls Royce Eagles would keep turning. On landing at Karachi, they were greeted with the news that Poulet and Benoist were in Delhi. Since leaving Cairo, they had cut the Frenchmen's lead to less than a day's flying time!

Capturing India's Taj Mahal on film, Ross Smith recalled it as the most memorable scene of the flight. He wrote: *There it lay below us, dazzling in the strong sunlight —a vision in marble. Seen from the ground, one's emotions are stirred by the extraordinary delicacy of its workmanship. Viewed from 3,000 feet above, the greater part of its infinite detail is lost, but one sees it as a whole. It lies like a perfectly executed miniature or a matchless white jewel reclining in a setting of Nature's emeralds.*

When the Vimy reached Delhi on November 25, thirteen days out from England, her crew learned that the Frenchmen had left that morning for Allahabad. After a night's rest, the Australians took up the chase. At Calcutta, the desperate Frenchmen had made a quick turnaround and left for Akyab (modern-day Sittwe) in Burma (now Myanmar), an hour or so before they landed. The Vimy challenge again almost came to a premature end as the plane took off from Calcutta in pursuit of the Caudron the following morning, November 29. Kite hawks soared above the aerodrome, and as the biplane climbed slowly over the trees, a hawk flew straight into one of the Vimy's propellers. Ross Smith recalled what a lucky escape it had been:…*had the propeller broken, nothing could have saved us from a terrible crash.…I marveled that our propeller stood the impact…one of the hawk's wings had become pinned in the rigging, and we secured it after the day's flight as a souvenir of a hairbreadth escape.*

CATCHING MONSIEUR POULET

As they approached Sittwe later that day, the Australians craned over the side for their first glimpse of the airfield. Keith Smith was the first to spot it. At one edge stood Poulet's tiny white Caudron. Eighteen days after leaving England, they had caught up. Ross Smith described the encounter: *Poulet was the first to greet us on landing. He came forward with a cheery smile and outstretched hand—a true sportsman, the hero of a gallant and daring enterprise. I was deeply interested in inspecting Poulet's machine, which was drawn up alongside the Vimy. In proportion, the contrast was reminiscent of an eagle and a sparrow. The Vimy towered above the tiny Caudron, which appeared altogether too frail and quite unsuited for the hazardous task these two courageous fellows had embarked upon.*

The following morning, Poulet took off an hour before the Vickers in a last valiant attempt to stay ahead. But the Vimy's vastly superior performance had put it an hour ahead of the

Caudron by the time both aircraft landed safely at Rangoon (now Yangon). The next leg, over mountains and impenetrable jungles to Bangkok, meant a certain crash for any aircraft forced down. In the interest of survival, the two crews agreed to make this part of the flight together. Although this meant the Vimy would have to curb her speed, it was a small price to pay for the mutual security the plan offered.

Early on the morning of November 30, the Vimy took off first and circled while Poulet prepared to leave. The Caudron failed to leave the ground. For twenty minutes the Australians orbited overhead and then finally set on course for Moulmein, across the Gulf of Martabab, in Burma. It was obvious that Poulet was not coming. They later learned that the Frenchman's luck ran out at Moulmein. Unable to get normal power from one engine, the French team discovered that a piston had cracked. Étienne Poulet's challenge was over —a bitter end to his magnificent salute to the memory of his friend Jules Védrines.

The flight to Bangkok was a nerve-racking experience for the Vimy crew. Ross Smith had to climb the aircraft up to more than 10,000 feet to avoid cloud-covered mountain peaks along the border with Thailand. Having reached the Vimy's ceiling, he had no alternative but to plunge through the cloud, where he was forced to fly with no "blind-flying" instruments. To keep the Vimy level, Ross Smith was thrown back on the "seat of his pants"—that uncanny sense of balance born of a pilot's experience.

A PERILOUS LANDING

At Bangkok, Bennett and Shiers were up all night regrinding valves on an ailing starboard engine. The next morning, December 2, they carried on to Singora (now Songkhla), a remote village in southern Thailand, where they came close to wrecking the aircraft landing on an ill-prepared airstrip that proved to be liberally studded with small tree stumps! It was sheer luck that the only damage was to the Vimy's tailskid, which caught on a stump and was ripped off.

Never having seen a plane before, the local villagers were at first terrified. When they saw the four airmen dismount, however, they lost their fear. Ross Smith wrote: *Several of them walked in front of the machine, flapping their arms and performing birdlike evolutions. We concluded that they were solving the mystery of flight and demonstrating how the Vimy flapped its wings to rise from the ground. My brother, unobserved, climbed into the cockpit and, seizing the control column, vigorously moved it to and fro, which caused the ailerons*

Poulet and Benoist held the lead in their fragile-looking Caudron until Akyab (now Sittwe), on the coast of Burma. Here, eighteen days after leaving England, the Vimy finally caught up with the Frenchmen. The Caudron had performed well until making a forced landing in India on November 12, the day the Vimy took off from Hounslow. From then on, plagued by problems, they took nineteen days to cross India, allowing the Australians to catch up and then race ahead. Poulet's gallant flight ended at Moulmein, 400 miles further south on the Burmese coast, when he retired with a broken propeller and a cracked piston.

Soldiers guarded the Vimy after the plane landed on an improvised landing ground at Singapore's racecourse on December 3, 1919. The crew spent the following day, Ross Smith's birthday, giving the Vimy a thorough overhaul. Ross Smith wrote: *We now had, roughly, 2,500 miles to complete, and in all that distance I knew of only five places at which a landing could be made; the rest of the country was either mountain, jungle, or swamp; so it behooved us to look well to our machine, for a single engine trouble and a forced landing away from any of these aërodromes would have ended all.*

and elevators to flap about. There was a wild scamper in all directions. We learned afterwards that the natives imagined that we were flapping our wings preparatory to starting off!*

The next day, while 200 convicts from the local jail cleared the tree stumps, Bennett located a piece of scrap iron and, with a hand-powered lathe, fashioned a new fitting for the tailskid. The Vimy and her crew set out for Singapore the following morning, December 4, in torrential rain. It was another hair-raising takeoff as they got airborne in a spray of mud only yards from the end of the waterlogged strip.

Reaching the British colony of Singapore that afternoon, Ross Smith was faced with more drama. He explained how his intrepid mechanic Bennett acted as a human braking system on Singapore's tiny airstrip: *I had been dreading the landing and take-off at Singapore, as the improvised aërodrome, the race-course, was altogether too small for our large machine. I glided the Vimy down at as low a speed as possible, and just before we touched the ground Bennett clambered out of the cockpit and slid along the top of the fuselage down to the tail-plane. His weight dropped the tail down quickly, with the result that the machine pulled up in about one hundred yards after touching the ground.*

From Singapore, the Vimy had just seven days left to reach Australia to finish within

the thirty-day contest limit. They used up one of the precious days on a final check of their machine before attempting the last 2,361 miles to Darwin.

FROM ROOFS TO RUNWAY

But fate had one more cruel trick up its sleeve for the Vimy's crew. On December 7, the aircraft became seriously bogged on landing at Surabaya, in eastern Java. The thin, dry surface of the airfield had cracked open under the weight of the plane to reveal a sea of semiliquid mud beneath. Following several abortive attempts to dig it out of the mire, the Vimy was hauled out by 200 locals onto a makeshift pathway of bamboo mats pulled from the walls and roofs of their own houses. Ross Smith described his despair at the setback: *I don't think I ever felt so tired or miserable in my life. There we were only 1,200 miles from Australia, we still had four of our thirty days left in which to do it. Yet to all intents and purposes we were hopelessly stuck in this quagmire without any chance of getting out of it. But just when things looked blackest a bright idea occurred to my brother. We knew that it was impossible to get off this aërodrome in the usual way, but why not construct a roadway of mats to prevent our wheels sinking into the mud and so get into the air?*

A friendly Dutch engineer helped pass the message around the nearby village. Recalling the touching scene he witnessed at the airfield the following morning, Ross Smith wrote: *Natives were streaming in from every direction bearing sheets of bamboo matting—they were literally carrying their houses on their backs—and already a great pile of it lay by the Vimy.*

The matting was laid in two strips, one for each pair of wheels, and the Vimy then taxied out gingerly along the improvised runway. All went well until the engines opened up for takeoff. In their slipstream, some of the mats blew away, tearing the fabric of the Vimy's tailplane. A tire was punctured, and the aircraft swerved off the bamboo strips and back into the mud. More mats arrived, and this time the makeshift runway was laced together and pegged down. As the villagers waved and cheered, the Vimy tried again. The plane gathered speed and lifted easily into the air.

SABOTAGE IN CRETE

The morning of December 8 was one of great rejoicing for the Vimy's relieved crew. Not so for the four Australians in the Blackburn Kangaroo, far back along the route in Crete. On the previous day, the 7th, the airfield at Soúda Bay had finally dried out sufficiently for them to leave the island, bound for Cairo. Fifty miles out over the Mediterranean, disaster struck. Copilot Williams was in the rear cockpit at the time: *I noticed*

Above: Bogged after landing at Surabaya, in Java, the Vimy was dug from the mud and then hauled by the townspeople onto an improvised parking area, which they covered with bamboo mats.

Below: Ross Smith's photograph shows the Vimy being hauled onto the bamboo runway. A similar system, using steel matting, was used to build temporary airstrips during World War II.

Rendle displayed superb airmanship nursing the crippled Blackburn Kangaroo back to Soúda Bay. Just clearing houses, the bomber hit a ditch and slewed towards a hospital, where it stopped nose-down a few paces from the wall. Although there was little damage, the crew could not obtain a replacement engine in time to reenter the race. The Kangaroo remained on Crete in a museum, vanishing during World War II, when, to keep it from the Germans, locals apparently hid it in a cave. None survived to relocate it.

that the tail was all black on one side. I guessed immediately this was from oil leaking back in the slipstream from the port engine. I passed a message forward on the pulley and wire system we used to communicate between the cockpits. Potts and I were together in the rear cockpit and Rendle was flying up front with Sir Hubert Wilkins navigating alongside. We tried to work out some idea that would help, but nothing was possible. Rendle turned back for Suda [Soúda] Bay, but with our contrary luck we were faced by a head wind and it took over an hour to reach land.

An oil line had fractured and was spraying hot oil under pressure into the slipstream. Aware that the Blackburn would not hold height on one engine, Rendle was forced to keep the failing motor going, throttling it back to the minimum revs needed to keep the struggling biplane flying level. As the

Soúda Bay airport boundary came in sight, the last of the oil was sprayed overboard. Within seconds, the dying motor raised a terrible clatter, followed by the scream of tortured metal as valves and bearings ran dry. Williams wrote: *I thought that the sudden locking of the crankshaft was going to cause the propeller to wrench the engine right out of the wing.*

The Kangaroo was heading for a group of houses, and a crash seemed inevitable when, somehow, Rendle managed to lift the crippled bomber. It grazed the rooftops and dropped out of control onto the other side, careening into a ditch. The tires burst, and the lumbering machine slewed off course and headed for the stone wall of the local mental hospital. It finally came to rest, nose-down and tail-up, just a couple of paces from the wall. The crew survived their narrow escape with only a few bumps and scratches.

A detailed examination revealed that the oil line had fractured at a fatigue crack caused by deliberately and repeatedly bending the line backwards and forwards. The evidence supported pilot Rendle's lifelong belief that deliberate sabotage had ended the Blackburn Kangaroo's challenge. But sabotage by whom? Rival pilots or aircraft manufacturers? This seemed highly unlikely. Jealous or disgruntled airport staff? Likewise, very doubtful. The embittered Bulgarian prisoners of war who had slaved away for days digging the aircraft from the mud at Soúda Bay? They had certainly had the opportunity and also had a possible motive, having been forced to labor for the sake of free and victorious Australian airmen happily heading home to their loved ones. There just might have been enough resentment among some of them to have sparked a desire for such bitter revenge.

ESCAPE FROM YUGOSLAVIA

By the morning of December 9, only two aircraft remained on the long haul to Australia: the Vickers Vimy, now heading for the Indonesian island of Timor, and the unlucky Sopwith Wallaby, still weatherbound in Europe and effectively out of the running unless the Vimy came to grief on the last leg. The sixth contestant, Lieutenant Ray Parer, was still in England desperately trying to organize a suitable aircraft.

A few days earlier, on December 1, fog and low cloud had forced the Wallaby's Captain George Matthews and Sergeant Thomas Kay to make an unscheduled landing in a pig paddock near Belgrade. Yugoslavia, like most of war-torn Europe, was still in a state of political turmoil. Patriots and revolutionaries vied for power as peace talks dragged on in an effort to hammer out the terms of the Armistice.

Within minutes of landing, the two uniformed Australians were arrested by Yugoslav soldiers. Accused of being Bolsheviks, they were promptly imprisoned in a tiny room in a nearby farmhouse, where for four days they were fed only bread and pig's fat. Unable to reason with their captors, the hapless Australians seemed destined to face a firing squad. Matthews and Kay decided their only hope lay in escape. Their chance came the next morning, when their guard was sleeping off the effects of a night's heavy drinking. The pair slipped quietly out of the building, and, expecting a shot in the back at any moment, raced to the Wallaby. The weather had not improved as they climbed aboard, but the fog was infinitely preferable to a firing squad. Fortunately, the engine started immediately, but its noise aroused the camp. As the plane roared into the air, a volley of bullets whistled around the fleeing airmen's heads.

Several more forced landings lay in store for Matthews and Kay, caused by lack of fuel and leaks in the cooling system, which were duly patched up with chewing gum, before the Wallaby finally reached Constantinople, on December 23. It had taken them two nightmarish months to cross Europe!

Following their arrest in war-torn Yugoslavia, George Matthews and Tom Kay managed to induce their Yugoslav guard to pose for this photo taken with Kay's trusty Vest Pocket Kodak—the Instamatic camera of the day. It shows the guard with Matthews and the woman who owned the house in which the crew of the Sopwith Wallaby were imprisoned. Explaining the reason for their surprise arrest, Matthews recalled: "After one look at our German maps they arrested us as militant Bolsheviks." Fearful that they were to face a firing squad, the airmen escaped after their guard went on a drinking binge.

We drank success to the last stage of the flight in the vintage of Timor—coconut milk. On the airfield at Atamboea, on the island of Timor, Keith Smith photographed (from left to right) Shiers, Bennett and Ross Smith before setting out on the final leg to Darwin—across the Timor Sea. The airfield at Atamboea, specially built by Dutch officials for the England–Australia event, had been completed only the day before the Vimy arrived.

LEG TO VICTORY

The Vimy reached Timor safely on December 9. The following morning, the hardy airplane took off on the final leg of the mammoth flight: the 466-mile crossing of the Timor Sea. The takeoff was another fingers-crossed affair, as Ross Smith recalled: *...I opened up the engines and just managed to scrape out of the 'drome. Scrape is exactly the word, for the branch-tops of the gum-tree rasped along the bottom of the machine as we rose. It was indeed one of the closest shaves of the trip....Then we set compass course for Darwin, and with a "Here goes!" we were out over the sea.*

Three hours later, they swooped low over the warship HMAS *Sydney*. At the request of Prime Minister Hughes, the Australian Navy had positioned the warship halfway across the Timor Sea, pointing south to Australia to act as a navigation aid and to be ready to help any aircraft that came down in the water. Waving sailors gave the Vimy's crew their first taste of Australia's welcome.

At 3 p.m. precisely on December 10, the Vickers Vimy's wheels touched down on Australian soil. It was the first aeroplane to land at the specially constructed airfield at Darwin's Fannie Bay. Ross Smith wrote: *Two zealous customs and health officials were anxious to examine us, but so were about 2,000 just ordinary citizens, and the odds of 1,000 to 1 were rather long for those departmental men, and our welcome was not delayed.*

First to greet Ross Smith was Australian Flying Corps colleague Lieutenant Hudson Fysh, who shook him firmly by the hand. Fysh and another air force friend, Lieutenant Paul McGinness, had slogged 2,000 miles across the trackless outback in a Model T Ford establishing a chain of landing sites for the race aircraft's "lap of victory" across Australia.

In the Air ~~Darwin~~
20/12/19

The Chairman
Barclay Tableland Council
Camooweal

Dear Sir,

Many thanks for your congratulations. I am very sorry we cannot land here for you all. We are dropping a sparking plug & a valve spring from our machine.

Yrs Ross Smith

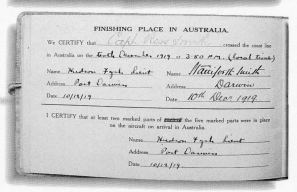

Left: Airborne radio was in its infancy in 1919, and the Vimy did not carry a radio. Short of landing, the only way to communicate with the ground was to drop a message, such as this thank-you note dropped to a well-wisher in Camooweal, a tiny town in the Australian outback. The "sparking plug and valve spring" were not only souvenirs; they also added weight, so that the message bag dropped to the ground and was not blown away.

Above: Competitors in the Great Trans-Planet Air Race had to carry a log book, which they were required to have signed by local officials as proof that they landed at particular locations along the route.

HMAS *Sydney* on patrol in the Timor Sea. The cruiser's role was to help any England–Australia crew in trouble. With her plume of smoke visible for miles, she also made an excellent navigation pinpoint on the long over-water flight. The Vimy crew were overcome by the sight of the warship's cheering sailors. *Perhaps it is not to be wondered at that the result of our snapshot was blurred through the shaking of the camera*, Ross Smith wrote.

The Darwin aerodrome had been built for $1,100. The landing ground at Newcastle Waters had been cleared by Aborigines, who were paid in kind with 2 bags of flour, 24 sticks of tobacco and 18 yards of turkey-red cotton. Nevertheless, one testy and shortsighted parliamentarian branded it all "an utter waste of money".

THE VICTORY LAP

On December 13, rested and revived, the Vimy's crew set out on a triumphant aerial tour across the outback to Sydney, Melbourne and, finally, the Smith brothers' home town of Adelaide. The 3,270-mile flight over Australia was to be punctuated with mechanical problems: the Vimy was finally feeling the effects of her epic flight. Near Anthony's Lagoon, 520 miles south of Darwin, the plane made an emergency landing after a propeller tip splintered in flight. Working in 100-degree heat, Shiers and Bennett performed miracles with glue and slivers of wood shaved from a packing case. For the delicate task of balancing the propeller, the resourceful pair mounted it on one of the axles balanced on two tripods fashioned out of tree branches. They then shaved the blade back to size with a broken bottle!

A week later, on Christmas Day, the port engine failed when two connecting rods broke shortly after takeoff from Charleville, in outback Queensland, damaging a propeller. The engine was taken by train to the Ipswich Railway Works, where it was rebuilt and a new propeller was made. The Vimy finally left Charleville on February 12, 1920, and, after an ecstatic welcome in Sydney, arrived triumphantly in Melbourne two weeks later.

Excited residents cluster around the Vickers Vimy at Darwin's brand-new Fannie Bay airfield. Ross Smith and his crew landed at 1500 hours on December 10, 1919, 27 days and 20 hours out of Hounslow. This was just 52 hours inside the time limit set for the Australian government's $50,000 prize. Only one other aircraft remained in the competition, the Sopwith Wallaby. It was grounded in Novisad, Hungary, where its crew were unable to get fuel.

Right, above: The first to greet Ross Smith (center) in Darwin was Hudson Fysh (right), an old colleague from the Australian Light Horse at Gallipoli and the Australian Flying Corps. Fysh handed Smith a bundle of telegrams, which can be seen in the airman's left hand. Following an official welcome by the Mayor and the Northern Territory Administrator, the airmen were carried shoulder high to the nearby jail and deposited on a tree stump, where the crowd demanded "Speech, speech!"

Right, below: Fysh and two companions traveled almost 2,000 miles overland to Darwin in a Model T Ford. Here, Aborigines help them negotiate soft sand. Along the way, they surveyed a route and established airfields for the race aircraft. Perceiving a desperate need for an air service in this remote area, in November 1920 Fysh founded the Queensland and Northern Territory Aerial Services, Qantas—today, the oldest airline in the English-speaking world.

Right: The Vimy's port engine had to be removed at Charleville, in western Queensland, where it failed shortly after takeoff on December 25, 1919. Ross Smith joked: *Perhaps the engine objected to working on Christmas Day!* As a somewhat shaken Shiers described the event, *[There was] a terrific bang and a flash of fire came out past Benny and me....we thought we were gone.*

Below: The repaired port engine ready for testing at the Ipswich Railway Workshops. With no spare parts in Australia, it took Bennett and railway staff a month to manufacture and fit a new cylinder, two pistons and connecting rods, six valves, a set of big-end bearings and a new propeller. The railway never sent the airmen their £1,459 ($7,295) bill.

Below: A poster advertising an illustrated talk on his flight from England to Australia given by Ross Smith. The "lecture circuit" was a significant source of income for the early aviators.

Above: The check for £10,000 presented by the Commonwealth of Australia was the equivalent of $50,000—a fortune in 1920. Ross Smith shared the prize equally among his crew, saying that *all [had] participated equally in the perils and labors of the enterprise.*

Below: A contemporary cartoon by Percy Leason reflects the general attitude toward the novel and risky business of flying. A handwritten caption reads: "Ross Smith's machine carries a crew of four. Rough guess at how they would be employed en route."

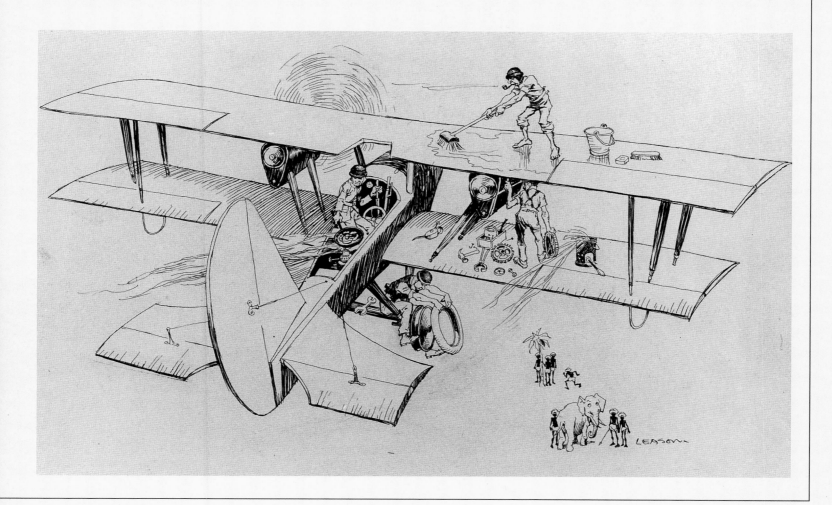

Right: The Vimy crew take morning tea in a small outback settlement during their victory lap across Australia. As only a handful of aerodromes then existed, the Vimy sometimes had to land in fields, and was often met by people who had never seen an aircraft. The route from Darwin to Adelaide was 3,270 miles long—further than the flight from London to Damascus.

Below: This remarkable panoramic photograph shows the Vimy arriving over Melbourne on February 25, 1920. Ross Smith had planned to reach Australia's temporary capital the previous day, but had been forced to spend the night in the small country town of Henty, in New South Wales, following three forced landings caused by problems with the port engine. As well as receiving the Australian government's £10,000 check in Melbourne, Ross Smith was awarded the Kodak Prize of £800 ($4,000) for the best set of negatives made by a competitor in the London–Australia race.

Opposite page, top: This evocative in-flight picture was taken by Captain Frank Hurley, Australia's foremost military photographer, as the Vimy flew through the "Heads"—the harbor gateway to Sydney—on February 14, 1920. Hurley joined the Vimy's crew at Charleville. As well as taking photographs, he took movie footage for a documentary film he made of the flight.

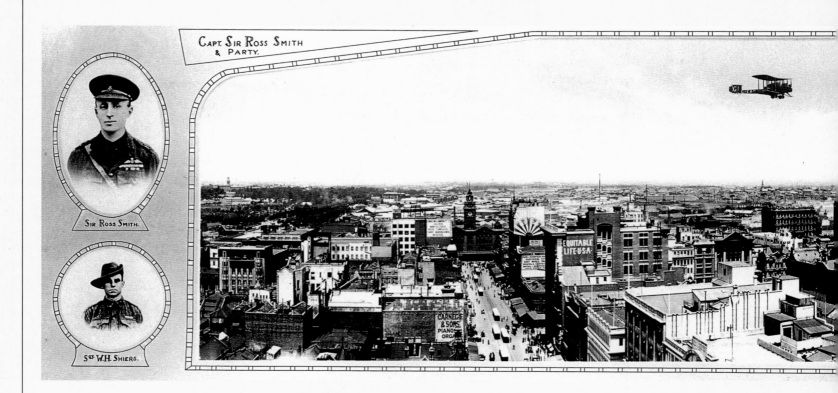

CAPT. SIR ROSS SMITH & PARTY.

SIR ROSS SMITH.

SGT. W.H. SHIERS.

ARRIVED AT MELBOURNE; FEB. 25, 1920

SIR KEITH SMITH.

SGT. J.M. BENNETT.

DRESSING FOR FLIGHT

Above: Sidney Cotton, inventor of the Sidcot flying suit, pioneered high-altitude, high-speed photo reconnaissance in World War II.

Peter McMillan wears one of the Sidcot No. 5 flying suits faithfully recreated for him and copilot Lang Kidby by Gieves & Hawkes of London's Savile Row.

Right: Harriet Quimby, the first woman to fly the English Channel, in 1912, poses with her Blériot, wearing the plum-colored satin flying suit she designed.

T HE EARLY PIONEERS took to the air in makeshift gear. Layers of everyday clothes, sometimes finished off with overalls and leggings, were topped with goggles and a check-pattern cloth cap, its peak invariably turned rakishly backward so as not to blow away in the slipstream.

By 1910, dashing French pilots like Jean Conneau and Jules Védrines were performing for adoring fans in smart leather outfits and fluttering scarves. Some, aware of the dangers, were even exchanging their trademark cloth caps for primitive hard-hat helmets.

In 1911, America's first airwoman, Harriet Quimby, came up with a natty flying suit of her own design. Made of plum-colored, woolbacked satin, it was a long dress with a monk's hood and drawstrings that ingeniously turned the skirt into pantaloons. In April 1912, to keep out the dawn cold when she flew the English Channel, she added "two pairs of silk under-overalls, a long woollen overcoat, a raincoat, and a sealskin shawl".

When these open-cockpit airmen went to war in 1914, their standard-issue flight clothing was mostly patterned after the wardrobes of motorists and seamen. Some added fur-lined boots and gloves, and layers of warmer garments they bought or captured. The less fortunate stuffed their flying clothes with newspapers.

A CHANCE INVENTION

The first really effective flying suit was designed in 1917 by Lieutenant Sidney Cotton, an Australian flying in the Royal Naval Air Service. Named the Sidcot, it was later used by Alcock and Brown and the Smith brothers, and remained in military service until World War II.

The suit evolved by chance following a two-hour patrol over snowbound France. Cotton's companions were frozen, whereas he felt quite warm. He was puzzled, especially as he had been tuning his Sopwith's engine when the squadron was scrambled and didn't have time

to don his flying kit. Instead, he had flown in dirty cotton overalls. He recalled: *Examining my overalls I found they were thick with oil and grease and I decided that they must have acted as an airtight bag which kept the body heat in*. When next in London, he had an airtight flying suit made to his design. It had a warm lining of woven mohair, then a layer of rubberized silk, then an outside layer of heavy cotton.

One of the manufacturers of Cotton's flying suits was the London tailors Gieves & Hawkes of Savile Row. They kitted out British Admiral Lord Nelson and African adventurers Stanley and Livingstone. In 1994, Gieves & Hawkes made exact replicas of the Sidcot No. 5 flying suit for the pilots of the Vimy, Peter McMillan and Lang Kidby, right down to the hand-turned bone buttons. They also provided the airmen with faithful copies of the Wolseley pattern Tropical Helmets worn by the Smiths in 1919.

Mechanic Tom Kay tries his hand at riding a camel during the two weeks he and pilot Matthews were marooned in a date grove on the shores of the Persian Gulf. Besides a shattered propeller and broken landing gear (which can be seen here), the Wallaby had a damaged nose section. The resourceful Kay used iron fence posts, scraps of wood and an old iron bar to effect repairs.

The England–Australia challenge was long over when Parer and McIntosh left Hounslow in January 1920 in a battered de Havilland D.H.9 biplane with the name *P.D.* They eventually reached Darwin after a seven-month epic that earned the pilot the lifelong nickname "Battling" Parer. The flight came to an end at Culcairn, in New South Wales, when, approaching in failing light, Parer picked a swampy field to land on and the de Havilland flipped onto its back.

Prime Minister Hughes presented the airmen with their cheque for £10,000. Showing a true spirit of comradeship, the four divided it equally between them. Hailed as national heroes, the Smith brothers received knighthoods, while Shiers and Bennett were given commissions for their valiant efforts. A month later, they flew the Vimy to Adelaide. Their 14,350-mile journey home had been completed in a flying time of 188 hours and 20 minutes.

STILL REACHING FOR HOME

The great Trans-Planet Air Race was over, but there were two brave footnotes. Matthews and Kay struggled on toward Australia in the Sopwith Wallaby. Following a crash landing on the shores of the Persian Gulf, when Kay performed miraculous repairs using old steel fence posts and an iron bar, they limped on

to Singapore with a badly warped propeller. But determination wasn't enough. Their flight came to a heartbreaking end in Bali on April 17, 1920, when engine failure brought them down in a banana plantation. They were just a day's flying away from Australia. The airmen and their wrecked machine arrived home by sea a month later.

All this time, the sixth contestant, Lieutenant Raymond Parer, had been trying to organize his bid. Parer and copilot Lieutenant John McIntosh eventually left England in a battered war-surplus de Havilland D.H.9 biplane on January 8, 1920. Even though the race was over, the pair were determined to fly home. It would take them seven months, in the course of which the airmen would virtually rebuild their worn-out machine three times along the way. But "Battling Parer", as he was

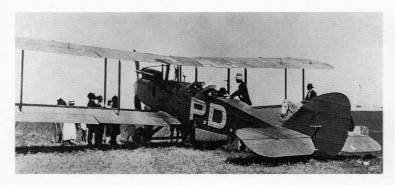

Above: Parer and McIntosh, here at Brisbane's Lytton Aerodrome, were sponsored by a whisky millionaire who provided only sufficient funds to purchase a war-weary D.H.9 bomber. Broke, and needing money for an engine overhaul and fuel in India, they turned their unairworthy machine into a flying billboard, plugging everything from tea to tires.

Right: Church bells rang and all Sydney stopped work to watch when the Vimy made its arrival. Here, beside Hornsby Lighthouse, Sydneysiders watch the Vimy fly over the harbor. "We thought we knew a little bit about flying, and so we just flew home," Ross Smith said with a grin at the Lord Mayor's reception for the airmen.

later nicknamed, would eventually become the second pilot to fly to Australia, and the first to do it in a single-engine aircraft.

A VICTORY FOR VICKERS AND ROLLS ROYCE

The Vimy's performance in the England–Australia flight had not just been a victory for its crew. It was also a triumph for Vickers and Rolls Royce. Combined with the Atlantic triumph, it helped Vickers promote their new Vimy Commercial, a modified, civilian version of the Vimy bomber, which sported a deeper, rounded fuselage and could seat ten passengers in the comfort of an enclosed cabin. In February 1920, a Vimy Commercial was one of four aircraft in a London–Cape Town race. It reached Tanganyika before crashing. Another contestant, a standard Vickers Vimy bomber named *Silver Queen*, came down south of Cairo. Her South African crew borrowed, and wrecked, another Vimy before reaching Cape Town in a de Havilland biplane. The Chinese government ordered forty Vimy Commercials, and the British air transport pioneers S. Instone and Co. Ltd. took delivery of one for use

Left: Rolls Royce placed this full-page advertisement in the London *Times* on December 11, 1919, the day after the Vimy's triumphant arrival in Darwin, Australia. The tremendous significance to the company of the record flights of that year is evident. The 360-horsepower Eagle VIII engines had been well proven, having exceeded their expected 100-hour life by 35 percent when the Vimy reached Darwin.

Right: One of the first to greet the Smith brothers at Sydney's Mascot Aerodrome was their mother, Jessie, seen here embracing Ross Smith, who was returning home after an absence of five years. Her Scottish-born husband, Andrew Smith, managed Muttooroo, a 3,000-square-mile sheep station in outback South Australia, where young Ross and Keith grew up with a thirst for adventure.

Jim Bennett helps a local politician aboard the Vimy for a joy ride in Queensland. He seems unconcerned about the close proximity of his arm to the whirling propeller. Ross Smith looks on from the cockpit, and Captain Frank Hurley operates his movie camera from the nose gunner's seat. Hurley joined the crew in Charleville to record the victory lap of the journey. He was a noted photographer in World War I, and took spectacular footage in the Antarctic with Sir Ernest Shackleton in 1912.

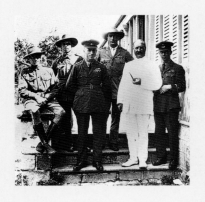

At Darwin, the Vimy's crew were greeted by the Northern Territory Administrator, the Honorable Staniforth Smith. The Administrator ignored the advice of an overzealous quarantine officer who had warned: "Don't go near them. You run the risk of a terrible tropical disease." Left to right: Bennett, Shiers, Ross Smith, Hudson Fysh, Staniforth Smith, Keith Smith.

on their inaugural Croydon-to-Brussels service. Other Commercials went to France and Russia, and an ambulance version was produced for the Royal Air Force.

Sir Ross Smith did not live to see the long-term effects of the great events of 1919. In 1922, he and Bennett were killed while testing a Vickers Viking amphibian. The brothers had planned to use a Viking to make the first flight around the world. Sir Keith Smith should have been on board but arrived late, just in time to see the aircraft enter a spin and dive into the ground. Ironically, Sir John Alcock had also died in a Vickers Viking crash, in December 1919.

A VISION FOR THE FUTURE

In Australia, where the flight of the Vimy G-EAOU had generated public excitement and a brief burst of government enthusiasm, *Sea, Land and Air* magazine editorialized: *The Vimy's flight did not restore confidence in aviation in Australia — it created it. They have blazed a trail from the use of which Australia will gain much, and they have awakened the nation to a keen interest in its own aerial development.*

Although the government was slow to realize aviation's immense possibilities, two men had their eyes opened almost immediately by the Smith brothers' inspiring achievement. Fresh from their overland mission to Darwin, Fysh and McGinness began seeking backers for a tiny bush airplane company they formed in November 1920, calling it Queensland and Northern Territory Aerial Services (Qantas). In 1934, after fourteen years spent conquering the vast distances of the Australian outback, Qantas spread its wings internationally and set out along the England–Australia route pioneered by the Vimy and her crew.

Years later, then knighted for his services to aviation, Sir Hudson Fysh recalled that historic moment in 1919 when the Vimy touched down at Darwin:

We anxious watchers at Fannie Bay at last saw the Vimy appear as a little speck away towards the Timor Sea and then grow larger and larger as it circled the ground and landed. It was one of the most moving sights I can remember—the termination of one of the greatest flights, if not the greatest, in the history of aviation…

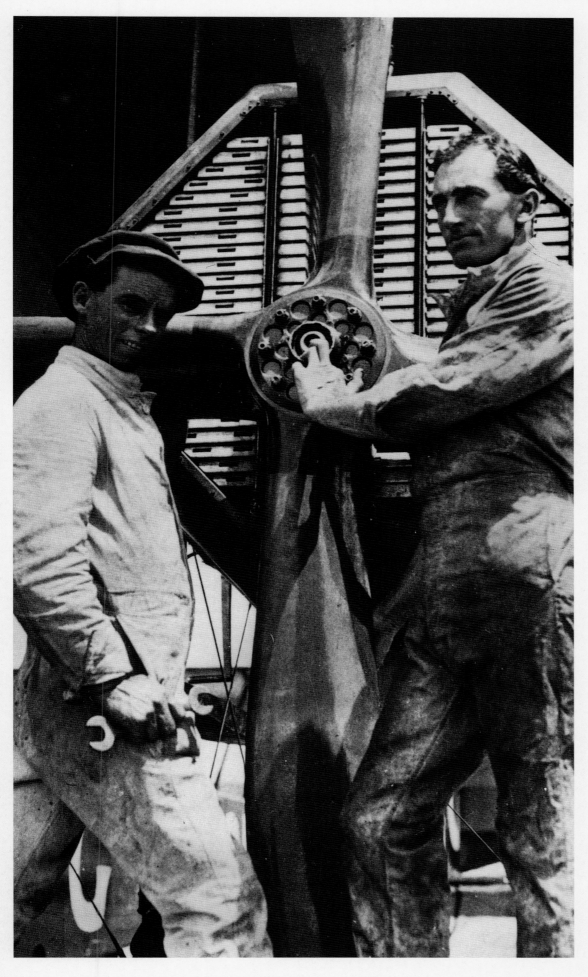

Walter Shiers (left) and James Bennett were the unsung heroes of the Vimy victory. The two mechanics are seen here working on the starboard engine at Charleville. Each had his "own" Rolls Royce Eagle engine to look after: Bennett the port engine, and Shiers the starboard one. Throughout the flight, they performed miracles to keep the engines running. In those days, 25 hours between engine overhauls was considered good performance, and even then there were daily adjustments to make. Between London and Adelaide, they kept their engines running for 188 hours, not to mention putting their lives on the line during several difficult takeoffs and landings. Years after, Shiers said: *Everything was worked in harmony. We each knew our job....Ross and Keith would say, "All we want from you two chaps is for you to give us the horses [horsepower]."*

STAGE ONE:
GOD 'ELP ALL OF US

STAGE ONE: GOD 'ELP ALL OF US

AUGUST 24 TO SEPTEMBER 18: ENGLAND–CAIRO

O N THE MORNING of Wednesday August 24, 1994, I was sitting in the cockpit of the Vimy as we flew at 517 miles per hour—sideways. Of course, she was dismantled at the time, and nestled securely in the belly of a gigantic USAF cargo plane. The C-5 Galaxy was gliding along at 30,000 feet over the Atlantic: a little easier than Alcock and Brown's crossing. The United States Air Force was bringing us to England to begin our great adventure.

Right: Close up in the Vimy. The crew takes the freshly reassembled plane from Mildenhall to North Weald in the blustery skies of East Anglia. The Vimy has a full complement of five on board, because, as Peter said, "We didn't have a rental car to move the crew around."

Previous page: Latitude 50°17'N, longitude 0°46'W Adventure begins as the Vimy climbs into the darkening skies of Farnborough, in England, bound for France. Bad weather would plague the team throughout Europe. The barely visible registration letters G-EAOU stood for "God 'Elp All Of Us", according to the 1919 crew.

Despite the bad weather, the pilots got a good view of the countryside, typically flying only 1,000 feet above the ground. "We were only going about seventy-five miles per hour, so we had a chance to study all the little towns and farms as they passed by," Peter said. "Sometimes I was mesmerized by the scenery, and would suddenly realize that I had wandered off course and hadn't checked the engine gauges out on the cowls for over fifteen minutes. It was such a thrill to fly the lumbering beast that my discipline lapsed a bit."

Touchdown was surprisingly smooth. The giant forward cargo door opened like a shark's mouth to reveal a beautiful, blustery English morning. Shortly after our arrival, the Vimy was disgorged from the Galaxy. Our crew of six, along with John La Noue and Dan Nelson, who built the Vimy, and dozens of helpers from the United States Air Base at Mildenhall, scurried and scavenged for the necessary parts and equipment, and had the aircraft largely reassembled within a few hours. We were raring to go, but we weren't going anywhere just yet.

On the way across, Jim Stanfield's keen eyes had proved to be good for more than taking pictures. He had spotted a crack near the hub of our number two propeller. This meant we had to get the spare over from Australia without delay. Two days later, the big, X-shaped box was at Heathrow, and just before dark, we were ready for a quick test flight.

THE VIMY RETURNS HOME

On a glorious Saturday morning, August 27, we said farewell to our tireless friends at Mildenhall and headed for Brooklands, near Weybridge, in Surrey, the original site of the Vickers factory. Lang was at the helm as we circled the East End of London, while I sat beside him navigating by the M25 motorway,

THE *Spirit* OF BROOKLANDS

The racing track known as Brooklands, built at Weybridge, in Surrey, in 1907, was the birthplace of motor sport and aviation in Britain. The first speed track to be built anywhere in the world, it quickly became the testing ground for those courageous spirits from around Europe who pioneered these two fields of human endeavor.

The airmen and motor racers would gather to discuss their ideas over simple fare at the Bluebird Cafe, located in the infield. On hot summer days, the dishes of jam on the tables attracted swarms of wasps, but the daredevil patrons remedied this by spraying the dishes with gasoline. The result fell short of being lethal, but gave a memorable taste to the strawberry preserves. As writer Percy Rowe recalled, Entrance demanded camaraderie, unselfishness, daring, mechanical knowledge, zest. It also helped to have taste buds that were not too demanding.

Vickers Aviation Ltd. was established at Brooklands in 1911. Soon, the company built a factory in the middle of the three-and-a quarter-mile racing circuit. Throughout World War I, they turned out aircraft for the Allied effort. A few years later, they manufactured the two Vickers Vimy biplanes that have gone down in the annals of aviation history: the first airplane to cross the Atlantic, and the first to fly from London to Australia, halfway around the world.

Today, part of both the high-banked motor-racing track and the aerodrome survives, and the Brooklands Museum has been established on a 30-acre site that includes many of the original buildings, now restored to their heyday condition. The museum has succeeded in keeping alive the spirit of adventure and innovation this historic place was built to foster. Brooklands remains a vivid reminder that, while time and technology change, the human spirit remains a constant, ever ready to attempt, and—often against the odds—to prevail.

often referred to as the world's longest parking lot. We knew we were in for a long trip when we saw the trucks below passing us with ease.

After thirty minutes above the motorway, I spotted the famous motor-racing track at Brooklands—the world's very first speed track—and, in the middle, the historic airfield, only 1,400 feet of which are now usable, where the first British airplane flew. As we passed overhead, I glanced down at the wall on the Byfleet side where Ross Smith fell to his death in 1922.

The brisk crosswind that was blowing, along with the tall trees we could see at the end of the snug little runway, made it touch and go whether we just closed our eyes at this point and hoped for the best. But, with only a few thumps and chirps from the tires, we crow-hopped intact up to the cheering crowd. The Vimy had returned like a homing pigeon to its nest.

Top: The Vimy's forward section is loaded sideways into the forward cargo door of the C-5 Galaxy that will carry her from Travis Air Force Base, in California, to the USAF Air Base at Mildenhall, in England. It was a snug fit even for the experienced Air Force loadmasters, with only an inch of clearance on the corners.

Above: Most of the 336 Vickers Vimys produced were built at Brooklands. Although disused for many years, enough of the track and aerodrome remain that visitors can easily imagine the roar of early racing car and flying machine engines. Occasionally, they get to see and hear the real thing.

Although the Vimy 19/94 project was spawned in America and Australia, I think Brooklands has always been our spiritual home. We spent the following week there. With the help of a dedicated group from British Airways Engineering, John, Dan and Duncan Audette worked on the cowls, coming up with a system of baffles operating in conjunction with a fan to force cooling air through the radiators. Meanwhile, my brother, Tom, and Robert Gieve of the London firm of Gieves & Hawkes set to work to design a cockpit cover to protect the Vimy's fragile instruments from the elements on the many nights our outsize craft would spend in the open, being too big for most hangars. We felt honored that this shield was being custom-fitted by one of Savile Row's best-known tailors.

After making a few more test flights around various parts of southern England, the Vimy was in fine working order on the following Saturday, September 3, when she was due at Farnborough for the biennial International Air Exposition.

THE VIMY BECOMES A CELEBRITY

The short hop to Farnborough was the last time Lang, John La Noue, Dan Nelson and I would fly together. On landing, Lang and I were rushed off to meetings and photo sessions, and had to leave finishing the Vimy to Dan and John. These two multitalented set designers really showed their stuff, putting in twelve-hour days in persistently foul weather to finish the cowls, the strut fairings and,

perhaps most vital of all, the elbow guards: those little tennis-net-like protrusions at each side of the cockpit that keep the occupants from having their arms shortened by the propellers whirling only a few inches away. She was officially named the *Shell Spirit of Brooklands*, and we proudly painted on the Shell logo at Farnborough.

Despite the howling winds and drenching showers, just about every one of the million visitors to Farnborough came by to have a look at the Vimy and offer us their good wishes. From the smiles on their faces, we could see that our audacious flying machine had done much more than recreate a period. She had revived a spirit of adventure that I'm sure many felt had been lost long ago.

I greatly enjoyed all the attention we were receiving, but after giving countless press interviews about our grand plans, I began thinking more and more, "I hope we can at least get across the Channel!"

CHAOS BEFORE DEPARTURE

By the end of the week, I was just about ready to swim across the Channel. On top of the chaos of hastily planning a trip through nineteen countries—a minor detail that had been neglected because of our hectic construction schedule—our entire team had only two days together before takeoff. Our support planes, the Australian Army Nomad and the Police Aviation Services Islander, arrived in the midst of a storm on Friday

A test flight over southern England. The pilots needed to get better acquainted with the aircraft, which flew only thirty hours in California. The throttle response was good, but acceleration was still sluggish from the drag of all the struts and wires. True to the original, the flight controls were heavy and unresponsive, with an unnerving lag-time between the pilot's input and the airplane's response. Another feature of the original that took some getting used to was the position of the engine instruments, visible on the side of the cowl. The four dials show, in descending order, fuel pressure, gearbox temperature, oil pressure, water temperature.

Top: The white cliffs of Beachy Head, in Sussex, recede as the Vimy sets out across the murky English Channel. The crew would see only cold, gray water for the next hour.

Above: September 11, 1994, 2:04 p.m.: The Vimy waits for her takeoff clearance before a crowd of 100,000 at the Farnborough Air Show.

September 9, and the three crews made each other's acquaintance shouting above the sound of the driving rain. Our first task, we realized, was to shed 1,000 pounds of equipment, and working out what lens would go with what case with what person in what airplane was like piecing together a 3-D jigsaw puzzle!

Before all the pieces were in place, we had to make a dash out into the dark to peg the Vimy down in a patch of grass. The wind had suddenly blown up, and was threatening to carry her away or even send her over on her back. We finally made it home at 11 p.m., weary and sopping wet, but we would soon come to accept this state as normal.

D DAY MINUS ONE
Saturday the 10th dawned bright and clear, but a series of fronts rapidly moved in, complete with thunder and lightning. We were scheduled for a flying display at 2:05 p.m., and as we rushed to move the airplane into position between storms, the tow vehicle tugged a bit too hard and snapped our tailwheel. I was devastated, thinking our

display would have to be scrubbed, but Dan came to the rescue with a miraculous bit of welding surgery. After the storms had passed, the Vimy made her debut as the last act of the day in front of a glorious setting sun.

CLIPPED WINGS
The big day had come at last. The morning of Sunday September 11 passed in a blur of activity. Press conferences, interviews, sharp jabs of remembering all the details I had forgotten, and goodbyes to loved ones, especially my brother, Tom, and his wife, Linda, crowded in one upon the other. Rolls Royce and Vickers hosted a brilliant luncheon, during which HRH Prince Michael of Kent, Gil Grosvenor, President of the National Geographic Society, and our other sponsors offered us words of encouragement.

In front of the assembled crowd, Major Mick Reynolds, the skipper of the Nomad, came forward to present me with a set of Australian Army wings for my flight suit. As I reached out to accept them, he quickly broke them in two and pinned the right half on my

THE EXPEDITION TEAM

*T*he Vimy was accompanied throughout most of the journey by two support planes, which carried the photographic crews and equipment, along with spare parts, baggage and survival gear.

The larger of these was a Nomad twin-engine turbo prop generously loaned by the Australian Army Aviation Corps. The use of the Nomad was arranged by Major Mick Reynolds, who skippered the aircraft. Mick was assisted by copilot Gary Tierney and their tireless engineer, Corporal Bob Shaw. The Nomad carried the National Geographic television crew, made up of director Christine Weber, a veteran of several aerial shoots in Africa, cinematographer Bob Poole and soundman Mark Roy. They were accompanied on most legs by National Geographic's number two photographer and photo technician, Joe Stancampiano.

Our second support plane was a BN-2 Islander that came from the Police Aviation Services in the United Kingdom fully equipped with a good-humored and capable pilot, Ian Snell. The Islander served as the photo platform for National Geographic photographer Jim Stanfield when he wasn't riding with us in the Vimy. Also traveling in the Islander were copilot Mark Rebbolz, who handled the flight clearances and logistics; Sean Maffett from BBC Radio, who reported our daily progress to

millions of listeners; and Bev Kidby, Lang's wife, who kept track of the sizable bills we ran up en route.

The Vimy's crew usually consisted of me and Lang Kidby in the middle cockpit, and in the back cockpit, our mechanic, Dan Nelson. Jim Stanfield usually sat in the nose gunner's seat ahead of us, but on some flights, Bob Poole, Dan or Joe Stancampiano would ride up front instead. On longer legs, with a heavier fuel load, the Vimy could carry only two or, sometimes, three people.

The little seat in the nose was actually the most comfortable. Because the beveled bow of the plane forces the air over the occupant, there was little wind, and it was also well away from the exhaust noise. The middle cockpit was worse, owing to the resonance from the propellers whirling only inches away and the considerable engine noise. The rear seat was almost unbearable, being right behind the blast from the props and the exhaust. I don't know how Dan lasted up to eight hours at a stretch.

The crews of the two support planes endured the same uncomfortable conditions as did the Vimy's crew, since they usually flew with the doors removed to be ready to take advantage of photo opportunities whenever they arose, yet often had to quickly climb to much colder altitudes, above 10,000 feet, to gain the fuel efficiency necessary for them to make it to our next destination.

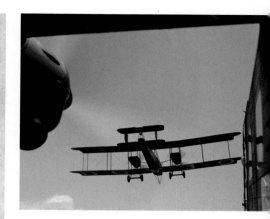

Left, top: The Vimy looks like a tiny dragonfly viewed from pilot Ian Snell's window in the Islander.

Above: The boxy shape of the biplane is framed by the Australian Army Nomad flown by Mick Reynolds.

Above: Flying in freezing conditions across the English Channel, the pilots wear oxygen masks not for breathing but to protect their faces from the bitter cold.

Overleaf: Dodging storms in the Rhône Valley of southern France, the fabric-covered craft is tossed like a feather as she probes a wall of rain, searching for holes in the weather in a vain struggle to cross the Maritime Alps and reach the safety of the Riviera.

85

Above: Navigating by rivers like the Rhône proved easier than map reading alone, since the soon-soggy maps were easily torn by wind whipping through the open cockpit. Flying along rivers also kept the pilots clear of hills in the event of worsening weather.

Right: Cloud-hopping near Valence, in France, the Vimy proceeds southward, but will soon be diverted to the west by lightning, heavy rain and black clouds in her path. The detour will force a laborious climb over the rising ground of the Massif Central.

chest. "You need to earn the other half, mate," he said. "I'll pin it on in Darwin." The spectators cheered with laughter.

Just before I was whisked away from the luncheon, with only thirty minutes to takeoff, I had a very special parting from my surrogate family in England, the Lumsdens, and from Tessa Barroll, the project manager.

Finally, Lang and I trudged across the grass infield, where Jim Stanfield and Dan were waiting. Our builder–mechanic Dan, who had hardly been out of California before, would be our indispensable companion for the duration of our journey. There were a few final goodbyes as we pulled on our replica Sidcot No. 5 flying suits. Lang was first to climb aboard. As I mounted the aircraft, I was slightly taken aback to see him flipping through the manual on how to operate the global positioning system (GPS). Seeing my surprise, he quipped, "No worries, mate. France is just over that way."

We did a few laps of the airfield for the massed crowd, and then landed. Most of the onlookers must have thought we had changed our minds and decided to call it quits. In fact, we were waiting to surprise the crowd with our ceremonial escort. As the Qantas 747 painted with stunning Aboriginal artwork came over my right shoulder, a voice from the tower crackled: "Vimy One cleared for takeoff to Australia!" I pushed the throttles forward, heard the unmistakable roar of our Chevy

truck engines, and in a matter of seconds the enormous wings lifted the four of us into a new realm of adventure. "One small step for a 747, and one giant leap for a Vickers Vimy," the tower added as a final send-off. "Have a safe journey now."

A NEAR-MISS AT THE START

"Turn left, turn left!" Lang suddenly shouted as we rose above the runway. "We've got to stay out of his wake!"

Lost in the magnificence of the moment, I was jolted back to reality. I pulled us to port, away from the vortices of air spinning off the jumbo jet's wingtips, and we set on course southeast, 135 degrees. The compass was wobbling all over the place, so I meandered while I tried to find our proper heading. Lang was getting impatient with my inability to hold a heading, but, about twenty minutes into the flight, he understood my problem when the compass danced off its mount on top of the instrument panel and landed in his lap. We then had to navigate by landmarks—which was fine until we came upon the gray expanse of the English Channel.

Our last sight of England was the striking cliffs of Beachy Head, in East Sussex. Then there was nothing below us but boiling seas for the next hour. I climbed us to 4,000 feet, where the cold was extreme but the turbulence bearable. For the first time, I knew how Ross Smith had felt: *The cold grew more*

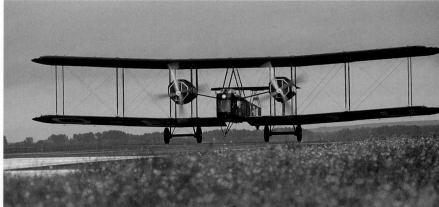

Top: Liftoff from Troyes, in the Champagne region of France. The World War I bomber departed with a peaceful cargo in her bomb bay: two magnums of bubbly, a gift from local vintner Pol Roger.

Above: A torrential downpour passed over Lyon, in France, delaying the team for more than an hour. Without enough daylight left to reach Pisa, they opted for Cannes. The attempt was ill fated.

intense. Our hands and feet lost all feeling and our bodies became well-nigh frozen. The icy wind penetrated our thick clothing and it was with greatest difficulty that I could work the machine. Our breaths condensed on our faces and face-masks and iced up our goggles and our helmets. (Ross Smith en route to Lyon, November 12, 1919)

The coast of France came as a welcome sight, although we had to plow through a few showers over the mouth of the Somme. Over the next three hours, I gradually got the feel of the aircraft and was able to enjoy the view. We floated past numerous postcard villages, most of them marked by the spire of an old stone church. Intermittent showers forced us back down to below 1,000 feet, and I'm sure the occasional French farmer who caught a glimpse of us must have scratched his head, wondering if he had just slipped back to the time of the Great War.

Our four giant wheels touched down on the grass of Troyes, in the Champagne region, at 7:05 p.m. local time. The mayor popped a cork in our honor in front of the small crowd that had gathered, and we drank a toast with my friend Patrick Albrand, who had driven from Paris with his family especially to greet us. But the celebrations were cut short as the skies opened up. We scurried to tie the aircraft down, with no choice but to abandon our luggage to the soaking rain.

Ross Smith's photograph of the French Alps. *Seas of clouds filled the valleys, with innumerable dark, rocky pinnacles piercing through and giving the whole scene the appearance of a rock-torn surf.*

DODGING STORMS ACROSS FRANCE

The torrential rains continued throughout the night, but by 9 a.m. the following morning, they had let up enough for us to push on toward our next destination, Lyon, 182 miles away. The winds had swung around from the south since the previous day, pegging our groundspeed back to 50 miles per hour. Having limited experience of the aircraft at this stage, we couldn't be sure we had enough fuel to make it to Lyon, so we opted to land in a small town in central France named Chalon-sur-Saône. It was here, as we slid off the narrow taxiway and got bogged in the mud, that we made our first acquaintance with the hazards of operating our big green beast out of small airports. With the

help of a few locals, we pushed the Vimy back on the asphalt and taxied her gingerly to the fuel pumps. We were then bribed with a cup of coffee to wait until a reporter from the town newspaper could come out to take our picture.

Now we were late for the official reception at Lyon. Airborne once more, we hoped to catch at least the tail end of the luncheon, but our pace didn't improve and we could see a large wall of storms looming ahead. We dodged back and forth, trying to avoid the worst of them, but to little avail. As lightning flashed all around us, we got a thorough drenching. One bolt struck no more than 20 yards off to the right of our nose. The normally unflappable Dan was riding

Left: Peter grips the controls tightly as rain slashes into the open cockpit. The whirling propellers act as waterwheels, showering the pilots, who sit motionless only 8 inches from the tips. The suffering was mutual, since the wooden blades were being steadily eroded by continuous impact with millions of tiny droplets, exposing raw timber beneath the varnish.

Above: The haven of an airstrip appears on a plateau near Mende, in the mountains of southern France. Unable to penetrate the storms, the Vimy flew 100 miles off course to the west. The big box kite became even more difficult to maneuver after acquiring several hundred pounds of rainwater that had soaked into the unprotected inner surface of the aircraft's fabric skin.

AGONY OVER FRANCE

The cold grew more intense. Our hands and feet lost all feeling and our bodies became well-nigh frozen. The icy wind penetrated our thick clothing and it was with greatest difficulty that I could work the machine. Our breaths condensed on our faces and face-masks and iced up our goggles and our helmets.

ROSS SMITH EN ROUTE TO LYON,
NOVEMBER 12, 1919

in the bow compartment at the time, and he looked around at me as if to say, "I hope you saw that!"

We pressed on through a sky that had turned an evil shade of brown, and eventually followed the Rhône as it wound its way past the ancient buildings of Lyon. We made a tricky downwind landing in front of a large crowd, and as I climbed out of the cockpit, soaked to the skin, someone handed me an umbrella! We had missed all the pageantry, along with the Australian ambassador and the other dignitaries, but at least someone brought us a sandwich.

I was adamant that we avoid flying through such heavy rain again, as I could see it was already starting to erode the leading edge of the propellers. But since the forecast was mildly encouraging, we elected to push on. If we could negotiate a line of storms to the south, it looked as though we would be rewarded with perfect conditions over the Riviera. Our folly in leaving the relative safety of Lyon would become evident all too soon.

We had made about 45 miles down the Rhône when approaching storms forced us to diverge westward over ground that was becoming higher and higher. More than once, we had to circle in a valley to gain sufficient height to cross the next ridge. We made a series of probes into the storms in the hope of finding a hole over the hills and below the clouds, but each time we were sent about-face, colder, wetter and even further off course. After

we had been in the air for three and a half hours, I checked the map, to find that we were only 15 miles closer to Cannes than we were when we left Lyon. At least Bob Poole, our cinematographer, blithely unaware of the very real perils we were facing, was thrilled with his first filming session in the Vimy. Eventually, we had the good fortune to find the haven of an airstrip among the rugged green ridges of the Massif Central. Lang put the Vimy down on a plateau overlooking the ancient village of Mende, and we regrouped with the crews of our two support planes, thankful to feel the ground beneath our feet again. Alarmed at the Vimy's poor climb performance through the hills, Lang and I discussed the situation with Mark Rebholz, the copilot of the Islander. We were undoubtedly carrying too much gear, but we also reckoned that the airplane had absorbed several hundred pounds of water from the inside, through the unpainted inner surface of her fabric skin. All we could do about this was hope that the weather would dry out! As we tied the Vimy down for

the night, we were doused by a shower that reduced visibility to something less than our wingspan, and once again set off in search of lodgings with our possessions drenched.

The morning of Tuesday the 13th looked more promising, with broken clouds overhead. Mark Rebholz and Ian Snell scouted ahead of us in the Islander, passing the word that, if we could climb to 7,000 feet, we would clear the weather and the mountains. It took us thirty minutes of ascending in circles around Mende to get up to this altitude, where conditions were smooth but frigid. Desirous of feeling our fingers and toes again, we descended as soon as we were clear of the high terrain.

PIT STOP ON THE RIVIERA

Over the town of Orange, we poked through a broken layer of cloud and spiraled down to 1,500 feet, seeking to escape the cold. Our groundspeed was poor, and we were spattered by an occasional shower. With visibility less than a mile, we scraped over one rocky ridge with only a 100-foot gap below the

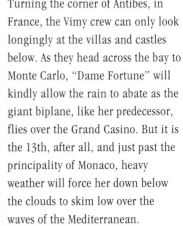

Left and below:
Latitude 43°44'N,
longitude 7°25'E
Turning the corner of Antibes, in
France, the Vimy crew can only look
longingly at the villas and castles
below. As they head across the bay to
Monte Carlo, "Dame Fortune" will
kindly allow the rain to abate as the
giant biplane, like her predecessor,
flies over the Grand Casino. But it is
the 13th, after all, and just past the
principality of Monaco, heavy
weather will force her down below
the clouds to skim low over the
waves of the Mediterranean.

clouds to fly through. Finally, we glimpsed the Mediterranean
in the distance and descended in a lazy spiral over Cannes,
gaining a magnificent view of the jetset city. I executed my
finest landing, but, to my great disappointment, there were no
starlets present and even the Geographic crews were off at lunch.

After refueling and waiting out a brief squall, we took off in
the afternoon and were soon passing over the Grand Casino of
Monte Carlo. I recalled Ross Smith's comment at this point in
his journey: *We swept round, looking for a landing place, for I
was inclined to test Dame Fortune and see if she would be as
kind to us at the tables as she had been to us in the air. There
seemed to be no suitable spot on which to land, however, so we
headed on to our course again, and soon our regrets faded in
admiration of the glorious coast-line over which we were
speeding. Suddenly I remembered it was the 13th; Fortune had
been kind to us after all.* It was the 13th for us as well, and I
felt doubly lucky knowing I was seeing the world pretty much
as Ross Smith had all those years ago.

On November 13, 1919, Ross Smith and crew circled above Monte
Carlo and the famous Casino, *which looked like a skillfully carved
and colored model rather than a real palace and its gardens.*

The weather was fair as we crossed into Italy, but as we neared Genoa, storms pushed us further and further south over the Mediterranean. At one point, we were 25 miles offshore, forced down to 300 feet by clouds and rain, and showing the groundspeed of a tortoise at 46 miles per hour. All my efforts were focused on keeping an adequate margin between us and the angry waves below. Suddenly, the engines coughed in stereo. I panicked for a moment, and then revived the spluttering motors by quickly turning the fuel selector to the number three tank, since we had just depleted number two. We lost less than 100 feet in the process, but I will never forget the look I got from Joe Stancampiano, who was on his first ride in the nose compartment.

My spirits lifted at the sight of four Italian destroyers streaming in echelon formation just off to our left. If worse came to worst, at least there was hope of rescue. When we finally cleared the corner of the slow-moving storm, we had to make a sharp left turn to get back on course to Pisa, which was 30 miles away. In clear skies, for a change, we made our approach to Galileo Airport. The air controllers asked us to circle the Leaning Tower, and we happily obliged in the golden light of a Tuscan sunset. Today had truly revealed that every day aboard the Vimy would be an emotional roller-coaster ride.

Several dignitaries were waiting to greet us, including the Commander of the Italian Air Force base there, General Domenico Mazza. The General was a former jet fighter pilot, and would come to our rescue soon enough.

ORBITING THE TILTED PYLON

The next morning, Lang and I took off in gusty conditions and circled the Leaning Tower twice before heading on course towards Rome, 182 miles away. I could tell that our groundspeed was meager when I saw a small red car pass us as it approached a stop sign. The driver proceeded through the intersection, pulled off at a roadside stand to make his purchase, returned to his car, and pulled away from us again. I looked in disbelief at the GPS indicator, which showed we were making only 24 miles per hour, indicating a 50-mile-per-hour headwind. As we neared the coast, the air became extremely turbulent. Lang turned to me, keeping both his hands on the bucking wheel, and said, "We'll never get anywhere at this rate." We decided to head back to Pisa.

Once on the ground, we put a few ropes on the airplane and contemplated our next move. Dan scavenged some equipment to solder a crack in the radiator, while I set off back to town with Peter Scott King of the British Consulate

Opposite page: The Vimy floats past the Leaning Tower of Pisa on the blustery morning of September 14, 1994. She set out on course for Rome, but severe headwinds and turbulence reduced her groundspeed to less than 25 miles per hour. Just 7 miles down the track, the biplane became almost uncontrollable, and the crew promptly returned to Galileo Airport.

Left: A ship leaving an Italian port recalls a quote from Ross Smith's account of his journey: *Below, a P. and O. steamer [was] heading south…Perhaps she is bound for Australia…my home and destination! With a smile, I contrasted the old and the new methods of transportation…Still, we wondered—unspoken the thoughts—who would reach Australia first.*

in search of a can of boat varnish and some sandpaper to spruce up the tattered edges of our propellers. Lang and I then got to work sanding the props and slapping on varnish, and we were ready for our second attempt by 11:30 a.m. As we pulled on our flying suits, a man approached us, introducing himself as a weather official. His English was heavily accented, but it sounded like he said there would be winds of 70 knots (80 miles per hour) and up to 50 millimeters (2 inches) of rain by mid-afternoon. I looked at him as if he were crazy, seeing the bright skies around us, and thought his English must be at fault. Just moments later, a gust of wind came up and shifted the aircraft back about 6 feet. "I'm not going flying in this!" Lang shouted above the roar of the wind.

WINDS GO FROM NUISANCE TO MENACE

We pulled the Vimy behind the modest protection of a jet blast fence and attached a few tiedown ropes to her. There were several shabby-looking apartments only 20 yards away on the upwind side of the fence, and the sight of them was making me distinctly nervous. It didn't require much imagination to envisage a few loose roof tiles blowing off and putting holes in our wing fabric. The gusts were starting to become stronger and more frequent when a Lieutenant Colonel from the Italian

Air Force appeared and asked if he could help. Lang and I nodded, and gratefully jumped in his car to see the base commander about using one of the military hangars a mile or so away on the south side of the airport.

Arriving at the headquarters building, we bounded up the stairs to the office of General Mazza. With the angle of the windswept trees outside his window becoming more acute by the minute, the general immediately understood our predicament. He barked rapid orders at his entourage, who leapt out of their soft leather chairs and scurried away. I gathered that a few C-130 transport planes would have to be moved to make room for us in a hangar. General Mazza then insisted we join him for lunch in the officers mess.

On the way back to the Vimy in General Mazza's staff car, we could see the light poles swaying like buggy whips as a black wall of water approached rapidly from the southwest. The torrent was unleashed when we were about 100 yards from our ship. Fortunately, Mick, Mark and Dan had attached a dozen or so extra ropes to the Vimy and had also tied sandbags to her tail. Within the space of thirty seconds, we all looked as if we had been standing under a firehose.

There was nothing we could do now except hang on and hope. The Vimy strained wildly at her leashes, trying to get

Pitting muscles against the elements, Dan Nelson and the other crew members strain to keep the Vimy from sailing away like a kite in the 50-knot winds. During a brief lull, they quickly untied her leashes. There was a dangerous mile of open ground to the safety of a hangar, but the gamble paid off. Hurricane-force winds blew up just as the doors were closing.

airborne, and had it not been for eight of us applying our additional weight to the wings and tail, I'm sure she would have sailed clean away. The pounding of rain and hail on the wings made it nearly impossible to communicate, and I couldn't help but think of that weatherman, whose grasp of English and the weather was a great deal better than I had given him credit for!

After a nightmarish twenty minutes, when we hung on through gusts that must have

reached 60 miles per hour, the wind finally started to abate. But seeing another wall of storm clouds rapidly heading our way, we decided to gamble on taxiing the Vimy across the airport before the next wave hit. My fingers fumbled with the knots in the wet ropes, but in a few minutes we were underway. Lang drove the plane, with Dan and me riding on the wings, ready to jump down and hang on if another gust blew up. The rain struck again as we stopped in front

The famous Tower of Pisa was built as a display of civic prosperity, but the marshy ground could not support its weight. Its lean has long outshone its splendor.

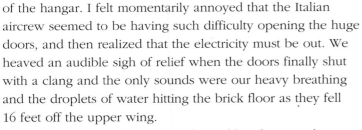

of the hangar. I felt momentarily annoyed that the Italian aircrew seemed to be having such difficulty opening the huge doors, and then realized that the electricity must be out. We heaved an audible sigh of relief when the doors finally shut with a clang and the only sounds were our heavy breathing and the droplets of water hitting the brick floor as they fell 16 feet off the upper wing.

General Mazza gave our waterlogged band a marvelous pasta luncheon, and we toasted him for saving the project. We felt almost gleeful watching the winds outside, which eventually hit 74 knots (85 miles per hour), ripping out hundreds of trees and

PISA WAS NO PICNIC IN 1919, EITHER

On our arrival at the hangars we found, to our dismay, that the aërodrome looked more like a lake than a landing ground....

[The plane bogged on takeoff, and tipped forward onto the nose-skid.] To overcome this difficulty, Sergeant Bennett applied the whole of his weight on to the tail-plane, and I once more opened the engines full out. Some of the Italian mechanics pulled forward on the wing-tips, and this time the machine started to move forward slowly. I suddenly realized that Bennett was not on board, but as I had got the machine moving at last, I was afraid to stop her again. I felt sure that he would clamber on board somehow, as I had previously told him that as soon as the machine started to move he would have to make a flying jump for it or else take the next train to Rome. We gathered way very rapidly, and, after leaving the ground, I was delighted to see Sergeant Bennett on board when I looked round.

ROSS SMITH IN PISA, NOVEMBER 15, 1919

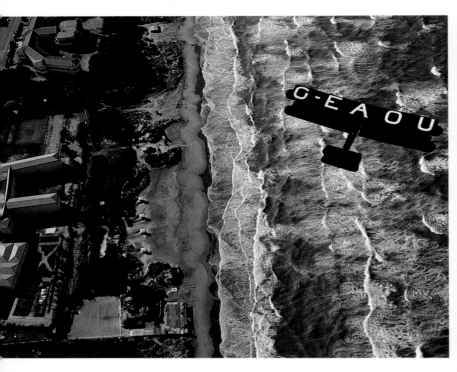

Above: G-EAOU proceeds south along Italy's beaches. The Vimy's slow forward speed required the pilots to angle her into the strong crosswind in order to keep a straight track down the shoreline.

Right: The Vimy orbits Pisa's pylon as if tethered to it by a string. Ross Smith and crew would have seen much the same view of the medieval city as they looked through their craft's struts and wires.

snapping a ten-story construction crane in half. A hurricane in Pisa? Who ever heard of such a thing? Now we know the real story behind the tower!

IMPROVEMENT OVER THE ETERNAL CITY

We left for Rome the next morning in bright skies. The headwinds were initially very strong, but our weather friend told us they would die down past Grosetto. Once again he was on target, and we arrived at our destination in time for a very friendly lunch hosted by the Aero Club di Roma.

At 2:30 p.m., Lang negotiated a tricky takeoff from the short runway at Urbe Airport. Tracking along the coast, we crossed the Bay of Naples, turned left over the Isle of Capri, and skirted the rim of Mount Vesuvius. Once again I slipped back in time, recalling Ross Smith's pictures of these landmarks.

Crossing the Apennines required us to climb to 8,000 feet and pick our way between the peaks and clouds. The terrain flattened out as we proceeded eastward, but the good weather we had enjoyed all day was about to change. We caught up to a squall line that obscured the horizon, and, plowing on straight ahead, soon felt the chill of rain being slung into the

Above: The hills of Basilicata. Map reading was difficult for the pilots in southern Italy, because every hilltop had a settlement on the summit, all marked on the map with a little cross indicating a monastery. They proved to be indistinguishable from the air.

 Right: Latitude 40°49'N, longitude 14°25'E
Pompeii the sequel? Fortunately for the Vimy, it is not an eruption but only cumulus clouds obscuring the rim of Mount Vesuvius. The plane is crossing the Apennines to Taranto.

cockpit by the waterwheels on either side of us. Fortunately, we had to endure only about thirty minutes of this before we landed at Taranto, in near darkness—the first Vickers Vimy to land here in seventy-five years.

There was a brief lull in the showers as we were met by our hosts at the Italian Navy base, Captains Bonita and Panico, immaculate in their crisp white uniforms. They found a hangar for us, but not before a sudden downpour drenched us and our bags—the first rain they had had in Taranto in four months! The prospect of dry clothes had proved to be a lost cause.

After the obligatory picture session the following morning, we pushed on for Athens. This leg began with a 70-mile water crossing to Corfu, which proved to be very fatiguing, as the horizon was blotted out by haze. In these conditions, a pilot has no clear reference to judge the angle of the airplane and experiences something like vertigo. I plodded along, staring at the instruments to maintain orientation, but allowed myself an occasional peek over the side at a sailboat 4,000 feet below. The rugged north coast of Corfu reminded me of the tragic fate of Howell and Fraser, the unfortunate competitors who drowned here back in 1919 within a stone's throw of the shore.

A TRICKY LANDING

We turned toward the Ionian mainland, taking care to give sufficient berth to the hills of Albania only a few miles away.

As we paralleled the spiny ridges of Greece, the air became very turbulent. Descending over the Gulf of Corinth, we made a wide left turn into Athens airport. I knew the bumpy conditions would not make for an easy landing, but pitched against the wake turbulence of the large passenger jets as well, our lumbering box kite proved almost uncontrollable. I was giving her strong encouragement with my hands and my feet, but her response was sluggish at best. Her wings wallowing, the Vimy's four wheels touched down one at a time, leaving enough rubber on the tarmac to resole an entire basketball team.

The next day, facing another long water crossing to the island of Crete, we put on our life jackets and took off toward the north. But we hadn't quite said farewell to this ancient metropolis. With the tacit approval of the controllers, we headed into a screaming dive to make a flypast of the Acropolis—something that is strictly forbidden. I wished we could have made just one orbit, to take in the magnificence of the Parthenon, but that would have been really pushing our luck.

THE SIRENS ARE CALLING

With Lang at the helm, I got a spectacular view of the Greek archipelago as we flew overhead, with its azure waters, beach-fringed bays, and cliffs speckled with the characteristic blue-roofed houses built of white stucco. Sighting a palatial sailing yacht near the island of Milos, I truly wished that we had

CROSSING THE APENNINES

...even the mighty Vesuvius was buried somewhere beneath the sea of clouds; so, reluctantly, I turned away and resumed our course to Taranto.

Our course now lay almost due east across the Apennines; but here again the clouds had banked against the mountains, and only an occasional peak peered through them. Owing to the clouds and my scant knowledge of the country, I determined to fly low, following, more or less, the course of the valleys, which were nearly cloud-free.

From breaks in the cloud, the sun beamed down on to vales of great loveliness. Numerous small waterfalls dashed down the mountain sides, and streams like silver threads rippled away through the valleys. The lower steps of the mountains were terraced, and wherever a flat stretch of soil presented itself small homesteads nestled, surrounded by cultivation. Sometimes we would be only a few hundred feet above the ground when crossing the crest of a ridge; then we would burst out over a valley several thousand feet deep.

ROSS SMITH OVER NAPLES,
NOVEMBER 16, 1919

The steaming crater of Mount Vesuvius was buried under clouds when Ross Smith flew over it in November 1919. This contemporary photograph was taken from 500 feet.

time to stop and taste the life of luxury. But it was time to get serious, for we had 100 miles of liquid real estate to cover before we reached the safety of Crete. Our destination was Soúda Bay, which would be our last stop in Europe, just as it had been for the Smith brothers. In a much grimmer sense, Soúda was also the end of the line for the Blackburn Kangaroo, which crashed against the wall of an insane asylum on December 5, 1919.

We found the 160-mile-long island with little trouble and turned right down the coast, landing into a fierce wind on a clifftop runway above the bay. The elevation provided us with the additional challenge of a sharp downdraft on our final approach, and I noted the expression of surprise on Lang's face as he had to bring the throttles up to full power to prevent us falling short of our target and smashing into the cliffside.

The local officials greeted us with ouzo and small sugar pastries. We greatly appreciated the hospitality, but had trouble getting through to them that, in these gusty conditions, our most urgent need was for vehicles to tie our airplane to. Lang, Dan and I scurried about and found some sandbags to weight down the leading edge of the lower wing. A few hours later, to our relief, two forklifts arrived, and anchored to these, our bird could surely fly no more. Lang, Mick and I then paid a quick visit to the Allied and German cemeteries near Maléme, the resting place of so many brave young men who died in the brutal last few days of May 1941, during the German invasion of Crete.

 Left: Latitude 37°59'N, longitude 23°44'E Athens' urban sprawl surrounds the ancient structures on the Acropolis. The warming weather was comforting for the pilots, but impaired the aircraft's lift. The crews had to offload most of their personal gear in Athens, since the warmer air reduced the efficiency of the wings and engines.

Above: A bird's-eye view of the Bay of Naples, with the Isle of Capri just beyond, on the right.

FIVE HUNDRED MILES OVER WATER

I began the eighth day of our voyage, September 18, with great trepidation, since we had never before taken the Vimy aloft with a full fuel load. Filling the number four tank added more than 1,000 pounds to our total weight. With all tanks full, the tailwheel strut was creaking in agony. Fortunately, the runway at Crete was almost 2 miles long, and by the time we reached the end of it, we had managed to claw our way up to 400 feet. We kept struggling for more height as we paralleled the island's north coast, but could manage no more than 1,500 feet. We crossed over the island, dodging the highest peaks, and soon had nothing but 500 miles of Mediterranean between ourselves and Africa.

The straps on my life jacket were flapping in my face, and as I kept tucking them in, I was reminded that they represented a luxury Wally Shiers and Jim Bennett had had to do without on this same leg. Having blown up four tire inner tubes to serve as makeshift lifebelts, Wally was faced with a problem. Here is how he told the story in an interview: *...we were up about 5,000 or 6,000 feet and all of a sudden these blessed tubes started to move about. They started to come in, they started to shove up around us, they started to get obstreperous, and I said to Benny [Jim Bennett], "They're expanding, Benny! Blimey, what are we going to do?" He said, "Oh, we can't put up with this, Wal, next thing they'll lift us out of the cockpit,"*

and sure enough, one of them did bulge out that much that we had to get the jack knife and puncture it, so by puncturing that, there was one loss, so I said, "Here goes the lot," so we punctured the lot of them, and that was the end of our lifebelts in case of need.

THE WELCOME SIGHT OF AFRICA

For the next four hours, we saw nothing below us but the blue expanse of the Mediterranean, not a single vessel appearing until we were only a few miles out from the Dark Continent. As we made our descent into Alexandria, I was struck by the sour, dusty smell of animals mixed in with automobile exhaust fumes. Flying as low as we did in the Vimy, smells were something we were always conscious of. The French countryside smelled sweet in comparison with the smog of Athens, which reminded me of burning asphalt. Later, when we pushed on into Asia, the predominant smell was of woodsmoke, interspersed occasionally with the pungent scent of sulfur from bubbling volcanoes.

Landing in Alexandria, stiff and weary, we endured the usual bureaucratic nuisances and were finally allowed to depart a few hours later. We crossed the smoggy skies above the Nile Delta, and the day ended in Cairo, at a decrepit little inner-city aerodrome called Embaba. Stage One was over—after eight days of weather so foul we felt the worst must surely be behind us.

Above: God 'Elp All O...The letters disappear into the blackness of a storm cloud approaching Taranto, in Italy. Once again, the Vimy was a rainmaker. Italian naval officers said that this was the region's first storm in months.

Below: On Crete, Lang plans the long water crossing to Africa. Maps were folded to expose the entire route, since the 75-mile-per-hour breeze made it nearly impossible to refold them in flight. Today was a particularly good day to stay on course. "We'll be flying close to Libya, and we don't want to end up in Benghazi this afternoon," understated Lang. Dan double-checks his fuel calculations.

STAGE TWO: WIND, SAND AND ARABIAN KNIGHTS

SEPTEMBER 19 TO SEPTEMBER 26: CAIRO–KARACHI

CAIRO GAVE US our first chance to catch our breath and consider what we had learned to date. The good news was that we had successfully flown the Vimy in diverse and difficult conditions, despite our extremely short test period. We had flown a few long legs, with heavy fuel loads, and were getting familiar with how the aircraft handled and her limitations. I wouldn't say I was confident, but I was certainly no longer fearful.

Right: Prayer calls drifting across the Nile from the mosques of Cairo add to the mysterious aura of the great pyramids of Giza. "It was magical to wander around the pyramids at dusk," Peter recalls, "but when darkness fell, I picked up the pace as we passed several shafts leading into the ancient tombs. Not that I'm afraid of mummies, but..."

Previous page: Latitude 29°57'N, longitude 31°09'E
In the bronze light of an Egyptian dawn, the Vimy looks almost modern against the ancient pyramids of Giza. The big biplane is a reminder that seventy-five years is just a split second in this region's long history. Of the seven wonders of the ancient world, only the pyramids remain.

Above: Lang and Bev Kidby enjoy a cool drink in Cairo. Ross Smith would have repaired to Shepheard's Hotel, where he *[sank] luxuriously into the arms of a great and familiar lounge chair, and [yarned] over the events that had happened since last [he] occupied it.*

Right: Three men take a break in the shade. The pace of Cairo veers between the hustle and bustle of the *souq* and the languor of the local bureaucracy. Many businesses are closed for most of the day, opening in the late afternoon and operating late into the night.

The trickiest problem we had yet to conquer was the coordination of all three aircraft in flight. We had missed out on a number of good photo opportunities because of this, which was causing some consternation among the Geographic crews. The heavy loads the support planes had to carry required them to fly faster than usual, and this made it difficult for them to fly alongside us in close formation, since, fully loaded, the Vimy could manage a top speed of only 76 miles per hour. We managed to solve this problem to some extent by making the Islander the primary platform for still photographs, which took some weight out of the Nomad and left it free to maneuver just for the television crew.

What with these difficulties, along with having to chart a path through the complex bureaucracies of each of the countries we passed through, I was beginning to realize that, in many ways, the Smith brothers' journey had been much simpler than ours. The jungle of red tape we knew lay ahead of us was enough to make us all wish we were back in 1919, when the world map was so liberally splashed with areas of British Empire pink! The other disadvantage of the Empire's demise was that each of these independent countries had its own currency. We suffered daily confusion with regard to the different names and exchange rates—until, in frustration, Ian Snell dubbed them all "klebbies". The name stuck, and as we approached a bar in our newest city, we'd find ourselves asking each other, "How many klebbies does a beer cost in this place?"

The world had changed in other ways, too. From Cairo to Karachi, the state of regional hostilities forced us to take a different route from the Smith brothers. This came as a great disappointment to me, as I had longed to fly over the Fertile Crescent of Mesopotamia—the land between the Euphrates and Tigris rivers, in modern-day Iraq. The Iraqis had, in fact, invited us to fly to Baghdad, but as this would have required United Nations approval, we chose a less controversial route to the south that would keep us out of the path of any flying carpets!

The Geographic crews were naturally anxious to get some pictures of the pyramids, and we set about making the necessary arrangements for an early morning photo flight from Embaba on the morning of the 19th. With the help of Paul Strickland from the Australian Embassy, we cleared the flight with the Civil Aviation branch, the Egyptian Air Force and the controllers at Cairo International Airport. Finally, we slipped a modest bribe to Farouk, the airport administrator, to persuade him to open the airport at 6 a.m. rather than the usual 8 a.m. Everything seemed to be in place as we made our way that

Lang can never resist a flea market or bazaar. "Aladdin's lamp must be somewhere in all this lot," he mutters aloud. "A miracle," the proprietor says, appearing at his side, "but a man brought in a priceless lamp only this morning, and I must not be caught with it. Please, steal it from me for only fifty Egyptian pounds."

Sitting on Shepheard's verandah, Ross Smith listened to the *strange blend of street cries—a veritable kaleidoscope of sound—that may be heard nowhere else save in Cairo.*

night to our hotel, the Mena House Oberoi. This former palace near the pyramids was the venue for high-level conferences during both world wars.

THE LAST WONDER OF THE ANCIENT WORLD

Early the next morning, I was awakened by the unmistakable hum of the Vimy's engines mixed in with the haunting sound of prayer calls drifting across the Nile from the mosques on the other side. I dashed up to the roof, and had to pinch myself to make sure I wasn't dreaming! There she was, the object of my obsession, circling the last wonder of the ancient world. I couldn't help but marvel at our audacity in bringing this adventurous vessel back to life seventy-five years after she had made her first flight over this mysterious landscape. I should add that the Vimy wasn't on autopilot but in the capable hands of our stunt doubles, Mick Reynolds and Mark Rebholz. Lang and I, still weary after yesterday's marathon leg from Crete to Egypt, had decided to skip the 3 a.m. wake-up call.

Overleaf: The monuments to the Pharaohs Khufu, Khafra and Men-kau-re cast beautifully geometric shadows in the early morning light. The peaceful moment was almost shattered by an Air Defense officer unaware that the Vimy had been cleared for this flight over restricted territory, who sought permission to make an armed response.

109

The smog, sounds and smells of Cairo, together with the snail's pace of Egyptian bureaucracy, can be oppressive, especially to the traveler in a hurry. Poor visibility and red tape kept the Vimy and her crew hanging about for an extra day at Embaba Airport. The crew entertained themselves by practicing their throwing skills with a boomerang brought along by Nomad copilot Gary Tierney.

A NEAR-TRAGIC MISUNDERSTANDING

From where I stood, the morning's photo shoot seemed to have been a success. Little did I know that another kind of shooting had almost broken out. For the entire period the three aircraft were orbiting the pyramids, there was a battery of guns trained on them, poised to open fire. It seems no one had notified Egypt's Air Defence Force—a division of the Egyptian Army and therefore a completely separate outfit from the Air Force—and our planes had been blithely flying about in their restricted areas.

When Mark landed later that morning, he was met at the airport by Paul Strickland from the Australian Embassy.

"You really stirred up a hornet's nest around the pyramids," Paul said. "Egyptian soldiers are on their way out here right now."

"What do you mean?" Mark asked.

"Apparently, gunners in the Air Defense Force had antiaircraft weapons trained and ready to fire on all three of your planes."

"You're joking. We had permission to make that flight. We were talking to the control tower at Cairo airport the whole time."

"Maybe so, but nobody told the officer

Above: After a five-hour crossing of the vast Mediterranean Sea, the Vimy crew were happy to be above terra firma again as they passed over the fertile green valleys along the Nile. The welcome sight of the North African coast marked the end of the first stage of the journey—but not the last of the bad weather. Fog, sand and haze would be a menace for the next two days in Egypt.

The great pyramid of Khufu, with the Sphinx in the foreground, as pictured in Sir Ross Smith's article in *National Geographic*. Although asked repeatedly, the Sphinx refused to answer the riddle of the modern crew's fate. Maybe the answer was back in ancient Thebes.

commanding the restricted military area beside the pyramids. He was furious. He even asked his superiors for permission to shoot. You had better leave right away."

Fortunately, the officials of Egypt's Civil Aviation branch confirmed that they had given us clearance to film the pyramids, and we found ourselves the meat in the sandwich in the ensuing fracas between the civilian and military authorities. As tempers erupted, our gang seized the chance to slip out the back door and head back to the hotel.

These events would come back to haunt us the next day. We needed to depart Embaba Airport near sunrise if we were to make the ten-hour flight to Ha'il, in Saudi Arabia, before nightfall. The Governor of Ha'il, His Royal Highness Prince Mogrin bin Abdulaziz Al Saud, had arranged a grand dinner in honor of our

Overleaf: The giant box kite gathers speed for takeoff from Cairo's Embaba Airport. Although the Vimy was only making a 12-mile hop to Cairo International, her tanks were full, since there was no fuel for piston-powered planes at the main airport. The air controllers became exasperated when the aircraft could not climb to 2,000 feet, which was the minimum altitude required to intercept any of the approach paths.

At Embaba Airport, Dan Nelson tries to shore up the Vimy's tailwheel strut, which is sagging exhaustedly under the weight of 4,300 pounds (673 gallons) of aviation fuel. Most of the fuel will be needed to reach the next destination, Ha'il, an oasis town in north-central Saudi Arabia. His concern was not unwarranted, since the strut had collapsed and been repaired at Farnborough the day before departure.

arrival. To no-show this party would not only be an insult, but could jeopardize our precious flight clearances. As if that weren't pressure enough, we had to make a stop at Cairo International Airport to attend to customs, immigration and other formalities, all of which would have to run their course at the subsonic Egyptian pace. We knew we faced a near-impossible task.

The following morning, having once again offered Farouk an early-morning incentive, the three crews met at 4 a.m. to be ready for takeoff at first light. As six o'clock slowly ticked by, followed by seven o'clock, we realized that the unfortunate Farouk must still be smarting from the tongue-lashing he had received the previous day from the military authorities. To add to our anxiety, the already poor visibility was getting steadily worse as the murky Egyptian cocktail of haze, fog, air pollution and wind-blown sand thickened around us. By the time someone showed up at 8:30 a.m., visibility had dropped to less than 300 feet. I can vouch for this, as I was out on the runway practicing my boomerang skills with Nomad copilot Gary Tierney, and could all too easily hurl my curved stick out of sight before it came hurtling back.

By 10:30 a.m., the day was a lost cause. All we could hope to do was to shift the Vimy the 15 miles over to Cairo International once the haze had lifted. But even this turned out to be easier said than done. With our full fuel load, we had great difficulty in gaining height and only just managed to dodge some of the city's taller buildings on our way out. Visibility was still less than a mile, obliging us to make an instrument approach into Cairo International. The air traffic controllers were clearly exasperated by our sluggish performance, and I'm sure they expected to see

a blimp drop out of the mist! No doubt we had kept some of their bigger customers waiting in line.

To minimize the offence to our Saudi hosts and preserve our good standing, Mick took the Nomad on ahead to Ha'il with the National Geographic television crew on board. Feeling somewhat disheartened, I salvaged the rest of the day by catching up on correspondence, and then rewarded myself with a long walk around the pyramids and the Sphinx with Jim Stanfield and Tessa Barroll, Tessa having come down from London to join us. As I watched Jim move about with such agility to capture on film the last of the day's fading golden light as it reflected off the striking geometric forms of the ancient monuments, I was filled with admiration for his talent and experience. When dusk fell and prayer calls once again came drifting across the Nile from Cairo, I had a strong sense of having been carried back to the time of the Pharaohs.

A TEN-HOUR MARATHON

This time, we were ready—or so we thought as we sat in the Vimy's cockpit on the morning of the 21st, secure in the knowledge that our sponsors and other "handlers" had cleared the way for us. It seemed too good to be true as we taxied out for takeoff. Just as we were about to advance the throttles, we

Left: Peter plans the long flight to Ha'il from the back of an Australian Embassy staff car at Embaba Airport. But even the best-laid plans can go awry. He and his map parted company prematurely about thirty minutes into the ten-hour flight.

The sail-powered dhows Ross Smith saw gliding along the Nile can still be seen today. These lateen-rigged vessels carry anything from rice to tourists down the swollen river.

A coffeehouse in Basra, Iraq, at the southern end of the Fertile Crescent of Mesopotamia. Ross Smith found this region to be *a land of suspended fertility, where animation and prosperity lie for the time dormant…Turn back these tides into the veins of irrigation and…Eden shall be again.*

were suddenly instructed to return to our parking area and await further instructions. Lang and I were angry, and repeatedly asked the tower for an explanation, but the only response was: "Vimy One, stand by."

After some curt exchanges over the radio, it became clear that the fault was entirely mine. I had requested a flying altitude of 3,500 feet for this next leg, but our route was to take us over some sensitive military areas, where the authorities required a minimum height of 11,000 feet. I duly apologized, promising that we would fly at whatever height they requested, even though I knew full well that getting the Vimy airborne in these conditions would be a major achievement in itself.

The air was thick and brown as we took off, and we struggled our way up to 1,800 feet solely by instruments. This was just high enough to get us clear of the blinding, sandblasted haze. The radar operators kept up a constant interrogation about our altitude, but we weren't about to tell them that the highest we could go was 2,000 feet. Our location was another matter. We couldn't very well disguise that, and we soon realized that they were pushing us further and further south of our intended route.

Starting to plot our new course, I leaned over the side, vainly looking for a point of reference on the desert sands

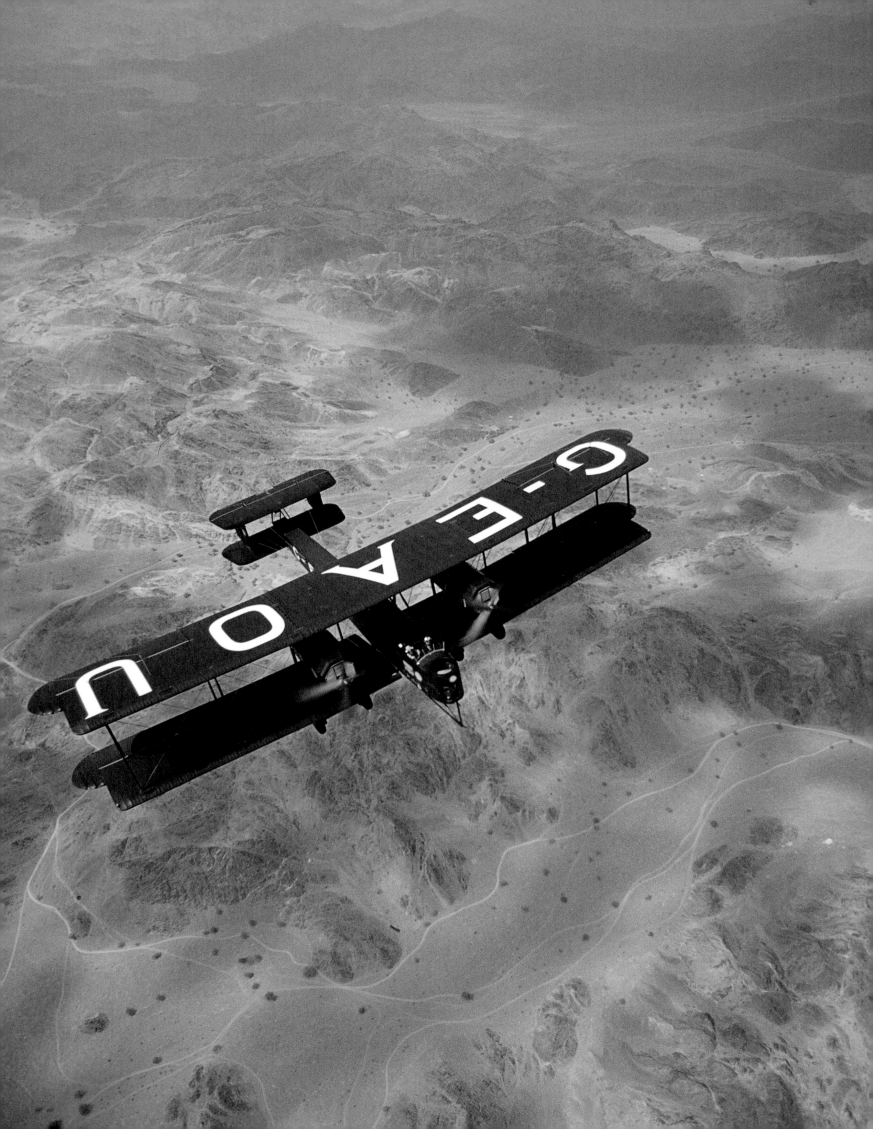

below. When I came back to my clipboard, I saw, to my dismay, that my chief means of navigation had disappeared! Frantically, I fumbled through all the pockets and pouches I could find, but there was no getting round it—I had lost the one and only map we had of this region, which contained crucial information relating to checkpoints and restricted military areas. After running through every possible excuse in my mind, I sheepishly turned to Lang and confessed. "It just flew out the top," I said. "It's these flimsy little maps they make these days!" Lang rolled his eyes, but took it in his stride.

Without the map, we had no choice but to fly low, below the radar, to conceal our location. We simply had to take our chances that we wouldn't stir up any hostile response from the ground. The mountainous terrain just west of the Red Sea was higher and more dramatic than I had expected, and Lang had to negotiate a path through whatever gorges we could find. With more than 2 tons of fuel on board, we were still slow and heavy.

Leaving the safety of land over Hurgadah, just south of Sinai, we crossed the Red Sea. Although momentarily mesmerized by the piercing, if unexpected, shade of blue beneath us, I was very much on edge after all the frustrations of the day. But my anxiety level still had a few notches in reserve, as I discovered when I saw the fuel pressure gauge on our right engine starting to flicker. I told myself it might just be a worn-out spring or a little air bubble in the fuel line, but I barely took my eyes off that tiny, fluctuating needle for the next three hours.

OVER THE LAND OF LAWRENCE

When the little town of Wejh, in Saudi Arabia, finally came into view, it couldn't have been a more welcome sight. As relief flooded through me, my thoughts were freed to drift back in time to the legendary exploits of Lawrence of Arabia in these parts. It was near here, during the Great War, that Lawrence's

Opposite page: The Vimy passes over the broad expanses of the Nafud desert, in northern Saudi Arabia. An occasional cluster of Bedouin tents was the only evidence of human habitation. Unsure of their reception, the crew gave the Bedouins a wide berth, particularly since the tribesmen's goats, being herded together at the end of the day, were easily startled and scattered by the Vimy's engine noise.

Above, left: "Insha' Allah!" ("As God wishes!") are the customary words of greeting in the Middle East.

The Deputy Governor of Ha'il province, His Excellency Hamad Rasheu Abu Nayyan (right), was among the dignitaries from north-central Saudi Arabia who welcomed the Vimy pilots.

Above, right: After a marathon flight from Cairo to Ha'il, Peter and Lang were given a warm welcome. Almost deaf after ten hours in the Vimy's open cockpit, Peter struggles to hear and respond to the questions put to him by his enthusiastic Saudi hosts, as reporters scramble for sound bites from the weary pilots.

The ancient ruins of Ctesiphon, near Bagdad, as Ross Smith saw them in 1919. In the center is the arched throne room where the mighty kings of the Persian Sassanid dynasty once sat.

119

Above: In the oasis town of Ha'il, the crew members are treated to an Arabian smorgasbord: a welcome surprise after a ten-hour fast in the aircraft. The normally reserved Saudis responded with enthusiasm to the Vimy and her crew.

Right: The sun retreats to the west through the wire cage that holds the Vimy's tail assembly together as the aircraft tracks east to Bahrain across the Ad Dahna' desert, in Saudi Arabia. The plane spent almost twenty hours in the air in the two days after Cairo, leaving the pilots wobbly and slightly deaf each night. But with the rigors of flying through Europe's perilous weather so fresh in their minds, Peter and Lang found fatigue a small price to pay at the end of a day's fair-weather flying.

Arab guerrillas had destroyed the Turkish railroads, and his personal pilot, Ross Smith, surely couldn't have been far away. I could sense his presence.

From Wejh, we turned northeast, winding our way through the rugged peaks of the Hejaz mountains, many of which topped 7,000 feet. Visibility had increased to a few miles here, and we enjoyed the stark and desolate beauty spread out before us—beautiful, that is, as long as we weren't thinking of landing. As the hours passed, the terrain gradually flattened out into the vastness of the Nafud Desert.

We were finally homing in on our target, the oasis city of Ha'il, but with 100 miles still to go, were forced to fly around the worst of a dry lightning storm, complete with blasting gusts of sand and extreme turbulence. Lang had been hanging on to the control wheel for more than nine hours, and I could see that fatigue was taking its toll.

We touched down at dusk, after a total of nine hours and forty-two minutes in the air. Several hundred white-robed Saudis with red-and-white-check ghutras were waiting in an orderly line to greet us. We did our best to be cordial, despite our deafness and our wobbly legs. In the hospitable way of these desert people, we were immediately offered bowls of dates and soft drinks, and I was soon feeling fine again—except when I touched the remains of my sun-scorched nose! As we tied the aircraft down for the night, I discovered the tattered pieces of the missing map wedged in the wires of the tail assembly.

CAPTAIN ROSS SMITH

M.C. AND BAR, D.F.C. AND TWO BARS,
AFC, ORDER OF EL NAHDA

"His cheerful and indomitable courage was a factor that was invaluable to us all in Palestine."

BRIGADIER GENERAL A. E. BORTON

ROSS SMITH was born in Semaphore, South Australia, in 1892. He attended Queen's School, in Adelaide, where he captained the cricket and football teams and was a champion athlete. A member of the Australian Mounted [Army] Cadets, he joined the Australian Light Horse as a private at the start of World War I and served at Gallipoli.

Smith transferred to the Australian Flying Corps and gained his wings in March 1917. Australia's most decorated pilot, he was

Above: In just eighteen months' active flying service, Captain Ross Smith became the most highly decorated member of the Australian Flying Corps. His trailblazing England–Australia flight was one of aviation's true milestones. London's *Daily Telegraph* wrote his epitaph: "If ever a human being followed the maxim 'live dangerously' it was this gallant Australian."

Right: Smith and his observer, Lieutenant "Pard" Mustar, dressed for flight, stand beside a No. 1 Squadron Bristol Fighter F.2B. Commonly called the "Brisfit", the plane was rated by many pilots as the best all-round fighting machine of the war. Mustar eventually became a pilot and pioneered aviation in New Guinea during the gold rush of the late 1920s.

awarded seven medals for gallantry. He earned his first Military Cross when he landed his lumbering B.E.2 behind Turkish lines to rescue a downed pilot, holding off enemy troops with a pistol as his fellow airman scrambled aboard.

One of his three Distinguished Flying Crosses was awarded for forcing a German two-seater down in the desert. Smith coolly landed alongside, took the crew prisoner, and set their undamaged airplane alight.

WITH LAWRENCE IN THE DESERT

In 1918, Smith conducted clandestine missions with "X" Flight, a tiny detachment that flew in support of the daredevil Lawrence of Arabia and his Bedouin troops. As well as bombing the Turks, Smith and his observer, Lieutenant E. "Pard" Mustar, accounted for nine enemy aircraft. One morning, between snatches of breakfast, they brought down four.

Ross Smith nearly became a statistic himself in a lone fight with a German Albatross. The two airmen, firing continuously, approached head-on to point-blank range. Veering away at the last moment, Ross Smith was hit twice. One bullet furrowed his cheek, and the other

scored his scalp. He crash-landed back at base, covered in blood.

At the end of the war, he was awarded the Order of El Nahda by the King of Hejaz for "conspicuous gallantry on behalf of the Arab cause". When his unit was equipped with a giant Handley Page 0/400 bomber, Ross Smith was appointed its pilot.

A JEST MAKES HISTORY

Smith's dream of flying to Australia was conceived when he was invited to fly British generals Borton and Salmond from Cairo to Baghdad in the 0/400. Borton then suggested in jest that they fly on to India, "to see the Viceroy's Cup run in Calcutta". "Then, after that, let us fly on to Australia and see the Melbourne Cup," replied Smith. Incredibly, Britain's Air Ministry approved the plan, and Smith was dispatched by sea to survey landing grounds between India and Australia. Ross was devastated when their plane was later crashed in the northwest of India, while being used in raids against the Afghans. His disappointment was tempered by the news of the Australian government's England–Australia prize.

YOUNG MEN AT WAR

It's a marvel to me now that I was not killed a dozen times a day. I've forgotten what fear is…it never occurred to me that they might possibly get me…. Such is War. It's a feeling (and to me a delightful one) that I defy anyone to express. I felt absolutely bursting with life and energy, and I've never felt so vitally alive before as on that morning…

ROSS SMITH IN A LETTER WRITTEN TO HIS MOTHER FROM PALESTINE, AUGUST 4, 1916

Ross Smith (in pith helmet) with Major General (later Air Vice-Marshall) Sir Geoffrey Salmond, who commanded the Royal Flying Corps in the Middle East, beside the giant, four-engine Handley Page 0/400. Salmond was responsible for the 0/400—the only one in the Middle East—being lent to No. 1 Squadron, AFC. According to T. E. Lawrence (Lawrence of Arabia), the big bomber was "the apple of Salmond's eye". At war's end, Salmond accompanied General Borton and Ross Smith on their pioneering Cairo–Calcutta flight.

Like sundials, wild camels cast long shadows by which the pilots could practically tell the time. The "ships of the desert" proved unfazed by the passing biplane, and provided a welcome distraction for the crew. Despite the desolation, the desert geography was varied and quite spectacular. As the day wore on, the plane's broad shadow raced further and further ahead.

Sending the Nomad on a day ahead had been a brilliant diplomatic stroke, and Mick had revealed himself a born ambassador. He came out to greet us dressed in full Arab garb—an unusual honor the Saudis had bestowed on him. Nevertheless, we extended apologies to our hosts for our late arrival. The Saudis shed their traditional formality in their enthusiasm for our unusual flying machine, and truly understood the spirit of our adventure.

Before shoving off the following morning, we were treated to a sweet hot tea the Arabs call Saudi whisky. Insisting that one cup was not enough, my new friends handed another one up to me in the cockpit even as I was preparing to crank up the engines. Today was going to be another long leg, but as we didn't need to completely fill the number four tank, we were able to take Jim Stanfield along in the back seat.

SIGHTS OF THE DESERT

We had good visibility on takeoff, and could see miles ahead on course. This was an unaccustomed luxury. Just out of Ha'il, we flew over some eerily beautiful mountains and rock formations, followed by bright green circles of irrigated alfalfa fields, with large herds of grazing goats. Even from 2,500 feet, our engine noise and our broad shadow sent the goats darting away en masse like a startled school of fish, only to abruptly change direction at some signal known only to them. We passed over twenty or more Bedouin encampments, and I wondered what kind of reception we would get if we landed. I thought it probably wiser not to keep scattering their goats. Lang obviously had the same thought. "Better not go any lower," he said. "We don't need a bullet through the floor from some angry Bedouin."

The gold of Gulf oil tanks is a reminder of the source of much of the region's wealth. Before oil was discovered here, Bahrain's primary export was pearls harvested from the waters of the Persian Gulf. Now, the city is the bustling financial hub of the Middle East.

In the gilded reception room at Bahrain International Airport's new terminal, His Excellency the Minister Yousuf Al Shirawi (seated between Lang and Peter) captured the spirit of the Vimy adventure in his speech of welcome. "Man knows no exhilaration like that when he is close to danger," he said. The opening of the new international terminal at Bahrain Airport coincided with a large aviation conference and the arrival of the Vimy. "Arriving in Bahrain was a bit like coming home," Peter said, "because I had made three trips here in the past year recruiting local sponsorship. We were in need of the comforts of home after two fatiguing days in the air."

Wild camels proved to be less intimidated by our presence. Whenever we could see there were no tents nearby, I would ease the Vimy down to about 500 feet and circle a pack of them to get a closer look. The day passed quickly, and I could easily tell the time by the length of the shadows the camels cast on the desert sand. Watching the Vimy's boxy shape as our shadow rose and fell over the undulating waves of sand took me vividly back seventy-five years.

The desert was far from boring, offering wonderful variations of color and texture and a myriad mysterious shapes sculpted in the sands by the sirocco winds. Every time I turned around, there was Jim, busily snapping away. I felt warm and secure, droning along peacefully at 1,000 feet, and was comforted by the firm wadis below, most of which we could have landed on if the need arose.

FANFARE ARRIVAL
Dusk fell as we crossed Dhahran, and we arrived in Bahrain in total darkness. Lang and I slid down the turtledeck, to be met by the exhilarating blast of trumpets. An exuberant crowd

The Tigris winds like a huge snake through the land that was once the Fertile Crescent of Mesopotamia. The Baghdad of 1919 is visible in the foreground. It was near here that the original G-EAOU was severely damaged in a violent midnight sandstorm. Her crew had to repair several broken control cables.

Flying by feel. The lights of Bahrain were a gladsome sight after eight and a half hours' flying, particularly since the Vimy has no instrument lights. The crew were treated to a hero's welcome, complete with a fanfare of trumpets, as they descended from the cockpit. His Excellency Yousuf Al Shirawi, the Minister for Development and Industry, arranged the welcoming ceremony as well as a number of other special events during the three-day stopover.

surged toward us: men in formal, black and gold robes, Gulf Air stewardesses, young girls in traditional dress carrying small bouquets of flowers, and the familiar faces of our loyal supporters. His Excellency Yousuf Al Shirawi, the Minister for Development and Industry, was the first to reach us, smiling warmly as he extended his hand. Following just behind were Shaikh Hamad bin Ebrahim Al Khalifa, David Ryan of Civil Aviation Affairs, and Rod Taylor of Gulf Air–three of our most valued sponsors.

Inside the terminal, in a gilded reception room, the Minister made a short and touching speech in which he said that, of all creatures, only *Homo sapiens* seeks out danger in order to experience great exhilaration. I was fatigued and famished, but

I managed to say a few words to express my sincere gratitude to our Bahraini friends, who had so wholeheartedly embraced and contributed to the spirit of our project from its inception. I had made many visits here during the months of preparation, so for me it was like coming home.

SPECTACLE IN THE DESERT
The Bahrainis had planned elaborate festivities in the desert for the next day, September 23. At 2:30 p.m., we made the short hop to our desert strip, which had been marked out especially for the occasion. The sandy landing ground was short but adequate, and Lang wisely made a low pass overhead to assess

 Latitude 26°06'N, longitude 50°30'E
Spirited escorts for the guest of honor. Prize Arabian horses and riders from the stable of Crown Prince Shaikh Hamad bin Isa Al Khalifa trot alongside the Vimy. The Crown Prince himself would arrive later by more modern transport, flying his own helicopter. A crowd of perhaps 15,000 gathered to enjoy the desert spectacle.

the situation. We swept past a sea of people in flowing robes and several huge Bedouin tents. As we approached to land, he kept up a little extra speed to counter a stiff crosswind, and the soft sand helped slow us down. Just as we touched down, thirty or forty Arabian horsemen with rifles and ammunition belts slung across their chests spurred their mounts to full gallop and raced alongside us, their white robes rippling in the wind.

As the props stopped, the crowd surged forward. I jumped down to try to dissuade the spectators from igniting the fabric with their cigarettes as they poked and prodded at our wings. Many were signing their names on the dusty surface of the lower wing, and some even held their children up to make a small scrawl, or plant a footprint, on the taut green fabric.

The scene was a colorful but bewildering one, an explosion of strange sights and sounds. On one side, a troupe of Arabian dancers sang and swayed in perfect time to the beat of traditional drums, in what appeared to be some kind of war dance. In the distance, a large brass band, arrayed in full military regalia and accompanied by the sonorous drone of massed bagpipes, played a selection of marching tunes and nostalgic songs. The magnificent Arabian horses continued to gallop full circle around the aircraft, and I stood watching them, entranced by the turbaned riders in such sure command of their spirited mounts.

His Excellency Yousuf Al Shirawi, the Minister for Development and Industry, led us into a huge, airconditioned

The horsemen circle for a closer look. Captain Ross Smith would have been right at home in these surroundings, having fought in Palestine with the Australian Light Horse, and later flying missions with the legendary Lawrence of Arabia. The well-trained Arabian horses proved to be unfazed by the 16-cylinder roar of the Vimy's engines.

Traditional *al Ahrda* dancers chant and sway to the rhythm of drums and tambourines to celebrate the Vimy's arrival. Gulf Air and the Civil Aviation Affairs Department hosted a magnificent desert party, complete with huge ceremonial tents carpeted with Oriental rugs and a stunning display of Arabian horsemanship. The Bahrainis are imaginative and experienced hosts, their city having long served as a vital port for aircraft in transit from Europe to Asia.

tent elaborately decorated with Persian carpets, majestic sofas and ornate floral arrangements, and Lang and I spent a delightful half-hour there, meeting other dignitaries and sipping cardamom coffee. In the midst of this kaleidoscope of color, we did our best to answer the barrage of technical questions fired at us by the ring of white-robed men seated all around.

In the distance, I could hear the pulse of an approaching helicopter. The Minister nodded and said, "A special visitor has come to greet you." He then led me by the hand out to the chopper, which was still winding down. The pilot stepped out, dressed in an immaculate military uniform and wearing a beret. It was the Crown Prince, Shaikh Hamad bin Isa Al Khalifa. We gave him a brief tour of the Vimy, and I saw several people in the crowd reach up to touch him reverently. As we chatted with the prince, he summoned a rider from those around us with a wave of his hand. The

horseman, bowing in the saddle, brought a dappled gray Arabian to the prince. "Isn't this stallion beautiful," the prince said, smiling. "He is my favorite."

As the sun sank into the Persian Gulf, we rounded up the crew and the guards pushed back the sea of spectators. A crosswind was still blowing, so I had little choice but to take off down the gradual slope toward the tents and the crowd, despite the obvious danger this posed if for any reason an engine should fail. We taxied to the top of our sandbox, accompanied by the horsemen. For a moment I fantasized I really was Ross Smith, preparing to fly Lawrence of Arabia on another daredevil mission to drop hand bombs onto a Turkish train.

For the first 300 feet or so, the Vimy moved reluctantly in the soft sand. I could feel her skidding sideways as she was pushed by the strong crosswind. I held the throttles firmly against the stops, and we cleared the crowd

and the tents by the slimmest of margins. Unable to resist a peek over the side, I saw that the crowd had parted before us like the Red Sea. Some of them, at least, must have heard my sigh of relief as we pulled away.

It was good to have the next day free to relax and catch up on work that needed to be done on the aircraft. In the morning, we had the honor of being taken to meet His Royal Highness the Amir, Shaikh Isa bin Salman Al Khalifa, and His Royal Highness the Prime Minister, Shaikh Khalifa bin Salman Al Khalifa, who engaged us in a lively discussion about our experiences and the intriguing history of the Vickers Vimy.

FAREWELL TO OUR ARAB FRIENDS

That night, the three men who had dared to dream so boldly on our behalf: Shaikh Hamad bin Ebrahim (bin Vimy for this week), David Ryan and Rod Taylor, gave us a splendid "bon voyage" dinner. Their commitment to our success had given us the morale boost we needed at that point to pit ourselves against the unknown, but inevitable, difficulties we would face in the coming weeks.

We set off on Sunday September 25 into the hazy skies of the Persian Gulf. With nothing but water below us for the next

Men and women, young and old, all seemed to grasp the spirit of the Vimy's adventurous flight. Many names and greetings written in Arabic, along with a few children's footprints, were imprinted in the film of dust clinging to the aircraft's lower wings. Like the original G-EAOU, the 1994 Vimy was at home in the desert, having been designed to cope with unimproved landing grounds. Vimys were in service in the Middle East for more than ten years.

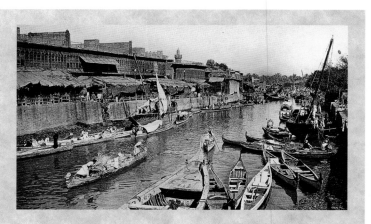

When Ross Smith passed through the port of Basra, it was the date-exporting center of the world. Modern strife during and after the Gulf War has scarred this once-prosperous port just north of Kuwait.

two hours, I strained to see anything of interest—a shark, a group of pearl divers, a shipwreck left over from the more romantic days of sail—that might distract me from the monotony of this long leg to Oman. After two hours, we made landfall at Abu Dhabi, and then crossed several miles of loose sand before we saw the craggy 8,000-foot peaks of the Al Akhdar mountains looming before us. I remembered having read that this mountain range is an ophiolite system, a section of ocean floor from ancient times that has been thrust up on land, allowing geologists to study its features up close. Suddenly, we began to experience severe buffeting near the highest peak, Jabal Asham. At one point, Bob Poole and his faithful movie camera were lifted right out of the Vimy's front seat.

Six hours and forty-five minutes after our departure from Bahrain, we touched down in the sultanate of Oman. Lang executed a respectable crosswind landing, and shortly after shutdown, we were met by a very tall, dark, turbaned man who welcomed us with a big smile and a handshake, introducing himself as Mohammed Ali Al Ryami. He and Jim Stanfield were old friends from the previous year, when Jim had come out to Oman to shoot a story for *Geographic*.

THE COLORFUL HISTORY OF THE SULTANATE

Mohammed moved us easily through the maze of customs, thanks to his job in the Ministry of Information. After a photo session for the benefit of the press and the Shell VIPs, we were immediately led off to a reception, where I was to learn some intriguing details about Oman from John Mills, Shell's local managing director and a keen student of the region.

Above, left: Peter and Lang are granted an audience with His Royal Highness the Amir, Shaikh Isa bin Salman Al Khalifa, who quizzed them about the Vimy past and present. "I will never forget the delightful smell of cardamom coffee," Peter recalls of meetings with Middle Eastern dignitaries. "We were entertained well beyond our wildest imaginings."

Left: Mohammed Ebrahim Khalifa Al Kadeer, a Bahraini businessman, gives voice to a traditional tribal war chant to celebrate the arrival of the Vimy in the desert.

John explained that Oman had never been a colony, despite the very British appearance of its police and military. It was set up as a British protectorate in the eighteenth century to provide a base from which to defend Clive of India's ships from marauding Arab pirates as they returned from the subcontinent laden with treasures. He also told us that oil drilling had not started in Oman until about twenty years ago. In fact, in 1970, the entire country had had less than 10 miles of paved roads. The current Sultan has greatly modernized the nation since seizing power from his father in a bloodless coup in that year. John's descriptions made me eager to get a look at the old fortress city of Muscat, but after a long briefing with the project team, I was so tired by the end of the day that I collapsed into bed and slept.

We left the next morning a few minutes after a glowing orange sun rose in the sky, passing to the left of Muscat and heading across the deep-blue water of the Arabian Sea, towards Pakistan. Although the atmosphere was hazy, I could see numerous ships below, both merchant and military, which provided a useful means of checking whether or not we were flying level.

After three uneventful hours, the Iranian coast appeared. We flew parallel to the coast until we crossed into Pakistan, passing over

The sun sets quickly in the lower latitudes. Beating a hasty retreat after a day of memorable pageantry, the Vimy makes a final low pass to salute the thousands of Bahrainis who came out to see her in the desert. The takeoff was far from routine in the strong crosswind, but the plane's primitive design proved well able to cope with the makeshift desert strip.

the border town of Jiwani. I couldn't find words to fully capture the bizarre and rugged appearance of this coastal terrain, but Ross Smith described it eloquently. With a good tailwind, we made our way over what looked for all the world like a barren moonscape. Jim was hopping up and down in the front seat like a jack-in-the-box, snapping pictures.

Near Karachi, we came upon an almost surreal vision in the form of ten or more container ships that had been purposely run aground on the shore below. Not unlike beached whales, they lay there in various stages of decay as they were gradually hacked apart with blowtorches and saws. All that remained of one ship was the little crescent-shaped remnant of the stern.

THE MODERN VICEROYS

We landed in Karachi seven hours and two minutes after leaving Oman, to be welcomed by fluttering banners and drifts of flowers. Our first engagement was a press conference held in

134

Left and below: Latitude 21°19'N, longitude 63°24'E Just across the Iranian border, in western Pakistan, the Vimy experienced severe turbulence stirred up by the desert winds blowing across the jagged moonscape below. The French pilot Poulet had his own problems here in November 1919, when he and his mechanic kept murderous tribesmen at bay with revolvers during two searing days and two sleepless nights making repairs to their plane.

CROSSING INTO THE SUBCONTINENT

Some of the country presents a remarkable sight, and appears as if a mighty harrow had torn down the mountain sides into abysmal furrows. Fantastic-shaped ridges and razorbacks rise precipitously from deep valleys barren of vegetation and desolate of life. Occasionally we passed over small flat plains dotted with abrupt hills and flat tabletops. The whole earth appeared as though some terrific convulsion had swept it and left in its wake this fantastic chaos of scarred mountains and gouged valleys.

ROSS SMITH
EN ROUTE TO
BANDAR ABBAS,
NOVEMBER 23, 1919

the old terminal rotunda, which would have been at home in the final scene of *Casablanca*.

That evening, a bus arrived to take us to the house of the Deputy British High Commissioner for a spectacular, 1919-period costume party staged in our honor. Hundreds of tiny oil lamps lit the quarter-mile driveway leading to a grand, pink stucco house in the distance. Fêted like conquering heroes, we were carried in triumph down the lane in horse-drawn cabriolets. On lawns spread with Persian carpets, men in white dinner jackets mingled with flappers in fringed skirts and headbands. All around stood enormous buffet tables bearing platters of curry, rice and lamb dishes. The head of the Shell company in Karachi, Tom Higgins, took us firmly in

charge, his dignified manner and deeply resonant voice reminding me uncannily of the late English actor Jack Hawkins. Everything conspired to reinforce the impression of being back in the days of the Raj.

The evening's festivities had been a fitting climax to the pomp and pageantry that had been so much a part of this second stage of our journey, but there was no escaping the problems of the present. One of the Shell representatives came across to me carrying a mobile phone. I spoke to his colleague in Delhi, who told us we might strike problems crossing the border into India. From this point on, we would find that our patience would be tested even more than our flying skills—but that's the way of the subcontinent.

STAGE THREE:
PASSAGE THROUGH INDIA

STAGE THREE: PASSAGE THROUGH INDIA

EVEN PHILÉAS FOGG, the irrepressible nineteenth-century hero of Jules Verne's *Around the World in Eighty Days*, knew that travelers have to prepare for unforeseen circumstances, such as acts of God, political turmoil and disease. But as we sat around at Karachi Airport on the morning of our seventeenth day, none of us could have anticipated anything like the convoluted chain of events that lay before us.

Right: Morning glory: *The sunlight sparkled on our varnished wings, and the polished propellers became halos of shimmering light. Our engines sang away merrily. The Vimy ceased to be a machine and pulsed with life, as if feeling the glory of the morning; my brother scanned the landscape below, plotting off the course on the chart and checking our position from time to time by villages and salient features, remarking how wonderfully accurate the world was created!* (Ross Smith, November 23, 1919)

Previous page: Latitude 27°11'N, longitude 78°05'E
Luminous in the dawn light, the Taj Mahal makes a stunning marker for the halfway point of the journey from England to Australia.

A vendor at the bazaar in Karachi, Pakistan. The sprawling port city of more than six million people lies near the Indus delta and teems with life at all hours. Formerly the capital, Karachi is still considered to be the business center of this Islamic country, although the capital was moved to Islamabad. Pakistan was part of India until 1947. There are several official languages in Pakistan, but the majority of its people speak Urdu.

The first hurdle was that the Pakistanis suddenly canceled our previously approved flight plan. We had intended to fly northeast up the Indus River to Bahawalpur, a distance of about 400 miles, and then to turn right to cross the Indian border, tracking directly east to Delhi. Because of troop encampments along the border, however, the authorities required us to fly over the sensitive Punjab region at 21,000 feet, which is a bit beyond the Vimy's reach. We considered fibbing, as we had to so many other controllers, but the Pakistani authorities had seen our aircraft and were unlikely to be fooled.

YOU CAN'T GET THERE FROM HERE

We were offered an alternative, southern route that had us crossing the border in a less sensitive area. But this posed a further problem. The Indian air authorities were still expecting us to arrive up north and hadn't yet responded to our requests for a changed flight plan. We had to come up with a solution that wouldn't see us stuck here for days, or even weeks, while the wheels of these two ponderous bureaucracies ground slowly on. To help us through this impasse, we had the able assistance of Group Captain Graeme Carroll, the Australian Air Attaché, who made a special trip down from Islamabad on our behalf.

The key was clearly to find a flight path acceptable to the Indian authorities that started from a point in the south where the Pakistanis would allow us to cross the border. We first applied for a path that would take us across the border and over Jodhpur direct to Delhi, but this was rejected as "too sensitive an area". Even getting this simple response took five hours. Later, the Indians countered with a compromise route: we could cross the border, proceed southeast to Ahmadabad, in the state of Gujarat, and then turn north to Delhi. This was an acceptable, if not exactly ideal, solution, as the

Left: Red-faced from long hours in the open cockpit, Peter naps in the V.I.P. lounge at Quaid-E-Azam Airport, in Karachi. There was ample time for resting between rounds with Pakistani and Indian officials as the crew sought an alternative flight path across the border to Delhi.

Above: Mick Reynold's map shows plan C: the zigzag path to Delhi skirting prohibited areas. Border tensions disallowed the northern route, plan A. Mick's middle finger is in the state of Gujarat, where an outbreak of plague stymied plan B. His pen marks the elusive capital.

total distance of 800 miles was almost certainly more than the Vimy could cover in the light of one day. But at least it gave us a route we could plan around. Gathering for the day's briefing at 2 p.m., we decided that the Vimy would need two days to fly from Karachi to Delhi, while the faster support aircraft, requiring only one refueling stop, would go all the way the next day.

This solution held up for roughly twenty-five minutes. Group Captain Carroll then came into the room to inform us that all flights into and out of Gujarat state had been banned as of today because numerous cases of the airborne plague had been confirmed in the region. We had already received several worrying reports of an outbreak of this dreaded disease, and now, it seemed, it was working its way northward, in our direction. There was a flurry of phone calls back and forth as we grew increasingly anxious at the prospect of being quarantined and ending up as permanent residents of Karachi or Ahmadabad.

The potential in all this for bad publicity stirred the Indian bureaucrats to a positively supersonic pace of decision-making. By midnight, they had found a zigzag flight path that would allow us to avoid both the military zones and the plague regions. Amongst ourselves, we half-jokingly wondered what altitude the authorities had assigned the airborne plague.

MORE THAN JUST FLYING

My brother and I generally filled the tanks, while Bennett and Shiers worked on the engines. It was not much fun, after piloting the machine for eight and a half hours in the air, to land with the knowledge that we had to lift a ton of petrol, besides doing innumerable small jobs, before we could go off to rest. In addition, we had to run the gauntlet of functions and ceremonies, and it was difficult to make folk understand that work had to be done. We deeply appreciated every one's generous kindness, but I fear that on some occasions people must have thought me very discourteous.

ROSS SMITH IN KARACHI,
NOVEMBER 24, 1919

Above: At a predawn hour in Karachi, Peter plots the estimated times between checkpoints along the Vimy's route to Delhi: a total of almost ten hours. Water bottles were nearly as essential as full fuel tanks, given the long hours of flying in the 80-mile-per-hour breeze, which left the pilots parched. Early starts were required, because the fully laden Vimy could not climb in the subcontinental heat of the day.

LONG FLIGHTS, LOVELY SIGHTS

With a bit of luck and some favorable winds, we knew we could make the slightly meandering route across the border and over Udaipur and Jaipur to Delhi before darkness. Taking care to max up on fuel, we staggered into the rising sun. It was a magnificent morning for flying, and the first two hours saw us over much denser and lusher terrain than I had expected, with long, green, parallel ridges not unlike a carpet that has been bunched up and is badly in need of being straightened out. When I saw ahead of us a narrow-gauge railroad, complete with an old-fashioned steam train inching along, I knew we must have crossed the border into India. It was like crossing back into the past as well.

Considering the diplomatic difficulties we had endured, I was surprised to see the scenery below us so peaceful and sparsely inhabited. We passed over many small villages, and at one point spotted an ancient sandstone palace tucked into a hillside, belonging, no doubt, to the local maharaja. Occasional patches of thick jungle enveloped the larger rivers, but as we approached Udaipur, the landscape became dotted with stark rock formations.

Turning north to Jaipur, we faced a new hazard: the sky was thick with kite hawks. We were slow enough to be able to dodge them in ones and twos, but occasionally we encountered a whole flock, in which case we had no alternative but to close our eyes and wait to feel the alarming thump. I'm sure more than one hawk swept between our wings.

Jaipur appeared on the horizon. I had no reason to expect anything more than another point on the map, but this elevated city presents a most striking sight, perched on a plateau with a lake in the middle and a magnificent pink palace built at the water's edge.

It had been a very pleasant but very long flying day, and I was getting pretty restless by the time we approached Delhi. On landing, we practically had to be hoisted out of the cockpit, and were greeted by an elegant turbaned man with a silver handlebar mustache. He was India's former Air Chief Marshal, and quite a hero, I was told. With him was the Shell entourage. After posing for a few photos and bypassing immigration, we were sped away for an audience with the Prime Minister, P. V. Narasimha Rao.

Jaipur, the "pink city" known for its buildings of that color, is the capital of the northwestern state of Rajasthan, in India. The city sits peacefully atop a plateau, with a lake in the middle overlooked by an ancient palace. Despite the serene setting, tensions were high aboard the Vimy as the plane dodged large flocks of kite hawks. The birds' predecessors in 1919 were not as fortunate.

CLOSE ENCOUNTER

A large number of kite hawks were flying round, alarmed by the size and noise of this new great bird in their midst....There was a crash as if a stone had hit the blade, and then a scatter of feathers. ... it was a breathless, not to say a terrifying, moment, for we fully expected to hear the crash of broken propeller blades.... (I have known so tiny an object as a cigarette end thrown carelessly into a propeller to cause the whirling blades to fly to pieces!)

ROSS SMITH
DEPARTING
CALCUTTA,
NOVEMBER 29,
1919

Lang and I were both extremely weary, but we were honored by the invitation and eager to assist our Shell host, Vikram Mehta.

We had barely left the airport when I looked up to see a large Shell billboard sporting a picture of the Vimy and the single word *swagartam*—the Hindu word for "welcome". Our car careened Indian-style around the streets of New Delhi, scattering scooters, people and livestock. Once inside the prime ministerial grounds, we were escorted through the first few checkpoints and then stopped at the innermost security gate. Here, dozens of guards were milling about with antiquated weapons. We received a going-over from no less than three metal detectors. By the third time, it had become a chore to have to

empty my pockets of all the leftover "klebbies" and the assortment of pins I had been given as souvenirs along the way. We were then led back out to an official car, which the security people proceeded meticulously to search with the help of special long-handled mirrors. Finally, the friskings complete, we were driven to the reception area.

We were ushered into a surprisingly plain anteroom. Lang promptly fell sound asleep, while I interrogated Vikram about Indian politics. About twenty minutes later, we were led in to see a casually dressed elderly man. The Prime Minister was politely interested in our adventure, and graciously posed for a few pictures as Vikram presented him with the obligatory silver platter for such occasions.

The Vimy strikes a tactile nerve in all who see her. Crowds everywhere, but particularly in India, left their names, along with greetings, in the dust that collected on the lower wing. An Indian soldier stands guard to keep locals in Agra from getting too friendly with the airplane. "More than once we stopped someone from putting their foot through the fabric as they tried to climb up on the wings," recalled mechanic Dan Nelson. "But we always tried to do this without dampening their enthusiasm."

Back at the Oberoi Hotel, we sifted through the details of the busy schedule confronting us over the next few days. Somehow, in the space of thirty-six hours, we had to fit in dozens of interviews, talks with local school children, a press conference, and two formal dinners, not to mention a photo flight down to the Taj Mahal and back.

What with trying to do right by our sponsors, keep the Vimy up to scratch, and catch up with a few friends, including Billy and Trish Campbell, who had come all the way from Los Angeles to greet us, as well as squeezing in a few hours for eating and sleeping, I was starting to feel rather overwhelmed. But what concerned me most of all was that, amidst the hype, I was losing touch with the adventure and my friend Ross Smith.

We met many amusing taxi drivers on our travels, but perhaps the most memorable one was our driver in Delhi, who, scattering all manner of living creatures before him, turned to me and Ian Snell to inform us, in that unmistakable singsong lilt: "To drive a taxi in Delhi, you need a very good horn, very good brakes and very good luck!"

The next morning was a mad rush through press engagements, followed by a trip back out

to the airport to meet up with streams of school children, who had lots of intelligent questions for us: "What altitude are you flying at?", "Are you cold in the cockpit?", "Where else in India are you stopping?", "What has been your favorite place?" Lang and I made the mistake of signing a few autographs, whereupon we were instantly mobbed by 500 nine-year-olds. I felt like Gulliver as the Lilliputians pushed me back against the Vimy's wings. Scribbling as fast as I could, I signed fifty or so outstretched scraps of paper before teachers intervened and herded the kids away. I swear that most of the pieces of paper I signed already had Lang's signature on them, so there must have been quite a few aggressive little devils in the crowd!

Night Flight

For our sunrise flight over the Taj, the only possible staging point was the air force base at the city of Agra, and we were fortunate that Chris Weber, with the help of our Indian Air Force liaison, Squadron Leader Kamel Deep, had secured permission for us to use it. We had planned to make a leisurely flight down from Delhi, but delays and interviews once again swallowed up most of the afternoon. Lang had generously offered to stay in Delhi for a V.I.P. dinner that night while I made the trip to Agra, and by the time Mick Reynolds and I taxied out for the ninety-minute flight to Agra, there were only twenty minutes of daylight left. We immediately decided to give it a go and risk a night flight rather than miss a once-in-a-lifetime opportunity of seeing dawn break over the Taj Mahal.

The light was rapidly fading as we steered south direct to Agra. We disregarded questions from the controllers about our location, since we were unable to read any of our instruments in the dark and were, therefore, illegally airborne. However, by dint of Dan shining his flashlight from the rear seat, at least we could read the engine instruments on the side of the cowls. Once in contact with the Indian Air Force base at Agra, I requested that they give us as much illumination as possible. They agreed to do this, and as Mick brought us down on our final approach, I found myself looking down on a runway lined along its whole length with flickering smudge pots!

This made a picturesque but potentially dangerous scene. The runway was surprisingly narrow for an air force base, and as we touched down, our lower wings passed a mere twenty inches or so above the flames. Thinking of our highly flammable wing fabric, I encouraged Mick to keep our speed up as we taxied half a mile to the end of the runway. We made the parking area without any burn-marks. Fumbling around in total darkness, we managed to secure the aircraft while simultaneously trying to explain our presence to the confused base commander, who had not been briefed about our arrival. He was, not surprisingly, pretty curious about this prehistoric bird that had dropped out of a moonless night onto his air force base.

THE PEARL OF INDIA

Taking no chances this morning, we arrived at the field with our Indian Air Force friend, Kamel Deep. At 4 a.m., KD, as we called him, was feeling groggy, but he "breezed" us through the paperwork in an hour. Climbing into the cockpit, I moved the control wheel to the right side, our normal procedure for close formation flying. We took off in a sky lit with a magical predawn radiance.

As we made our way along the course of the Yamuna River, the first landmark appeared in the form of the red blocks of Agra Fort. Then, as I banked to the right, the Taj Mahal was revealed, glowing pink like a giant pearl, 1,000 feet below us. I took a deep breath, reveling in my good fortune to be guiding this stately ship over the wondrous monument, and found myself repeating Ross Smith's words: *It lies like a perfectly executed miniature or a matchless white jewel reclining in a setting of Nature's emeralds.* I had not memorized these words, so he must have whispered them to me.

Delhi, the future capital of India, as seen from the Vimy's cockpit on November 26, 1919, thirteen days and 5,870 miles from London.

SAFER IN THE AIR

Further diversion, with less relaxation, was provided by the native driver of a car we hired. In the language of the realm in which we had been living, he navigated full out and nearly crashed us on several occasions, in his desire to show what a pilot he was. I declare that I "had the wind up" [was nervous] far more often on this bit of journey than during the whole flight. However, the casualties were few and the fatalities nil, and we paid him off at the R.A.F. quarters.

ROSS SMITH IN DELHI,
NOVEMBER 26, 1919

Ross Smith's picture of the Taj Mahal, taken from about 3,000 feet above the world's most exquisite architectural gem. His was the first-ever aerial photograph of the Taj.

Tracking down the Yamuna River, in India, brings into view the Taj Mahal, its dome glowing pink like a giant pearl. The monument was built in the seventeenth century by the Mogul Emperor Shah Jahan as a mausoleum for his favorite wife, Mumtaz Mahal. The spectacular sight was mesmerizing to the crew, who overindulged in the glory of the early morning flight. This left them with a serious problem, as they did not have enough fuel to return to Delhi.

JEWEL OF INDIA
Of all the remembered scenes, wonderful and beautiful, that of the Taj Mahal remains the most vivid and the most exquisite.... It lies like a perfectly executed miniature or a matchless white jewel reclining in a setting of Nature's emeralds.

ROSS SMITH
OVER AGRA,
NOVEMBER 27, 1919

147

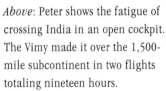

Above: Peter shows the fatigue of crossing India in an open cockpit. The Vimy made it over the 1,500-mile subcontinent in two flights totaling nineteen hours.

We made numerous gentle orbits, gradually descending as though tethered like a toy plane to the top of the great marble dome. I broke off at 500 feet, not wishing to risk an accident that might mar the flawless beauty. All of us were exuberant on our return to base, intoxicated by the rare privilege of what we had just experienced.

MYSTERY JUICE

Back on earth, the daily roller coaster was soon off and running once again, and I was jolted back to reality by the problem of finding fuel for our return to Delhi. I had underestimated our fuel requirements, and we had used up an extra 20 gallons overindulging ourselves on our flight over the Taj. This left us about 40 gallons short of the minimum we needed to get back. The Indian Air Force offered to track some down for us, but it soon became clear that that could take days. Likewise, Shell could send some fuel from Delhi, but that would also take at least a day. KD came back to us after only two hours, riding in a large Russian-built truck. In the back of this giant covered wagon, a small man in ragged clothes was squatting beside an empty 44-gallon fuel drum that looked as if it had been rolled here all the way from a Texas oil refinery.

Dan and I secured the necessary permits and climbed into the cab beside our driver, a young corporal. We bounced off down the dusty, corrugated road, scattering people, bicycles and livestock in all directions. It felt as if the truck was going to shake itself to pieces, although we couldn't have been going much faster than 15 miles per hour. A couple of miles on, we stopped at a filling station. Like many things in India, it had undoubtedly seen better days—but what really alarmed me was that there were no cars anywhere in sight, only scooters.

"What fuel is this?" I asked a man standing at the pump holding a cigar box full of rupees. "Eighty octane," he replied. "Sixty-five," said someone behind him. "What for?" asked a third. I didn't bother to try and explain. Having no other option, we began filling the drum, which was leaking like a sieve. Undaunted, our obliging friend in the back of the truck simply wrapped his arms around it and plugged the biggest leaks with his fingers and palms. Thus we trundled back to the Vimy, where Dan and Mick attempted to siphon the fuel into our number four tank with a hose borrowed from a maintenance man.

After a few bouts of sucking and spitting, Dan and Mick still couldn't get the fuel to transfer to the aircraft. I noticed that the residue on the ground did not evaporate. Not a good sign. Our drum was still leaking away any chance we had of getting to Delhi when an airport official came to our rescue with a rotating diesel pump. This enabled us to get most of the remaining mystery fuel into the aircraft.

Left: The old control tower at Calcutta's Dum Dum Airport is gradually being demolished. Such spartan facilities were the norm in the middle stages of the journey, as were the reams of paperwork required for each flight. Ian Snell, who filed flight plans for the group, was missing a vital piece of equipment. "I would have paid dearly for a piece of carbon paper," he said. "They demanded five copies of everything, and everything had to be stamped by customs, immigration, weather and the air force."

The busy harbor of Calcutta. Ross Smith, in company with Jim Bennett and Wally Shiers, departed from here aboard the steamer *Sphinx* on February 10, 1919, to survey landing sites between India and Australia for their planned flight to Darwin.

Ross (left) and Keith Smith stand in the Vimy's cockpit after landing at Dum Dum aerodrome in Calcutta on November 27, 1919. Wrinkles in the fuselage fabric indicate the wear and tear on the aircraft from traveling through climatic extremes.

RUNNING ON FUMES

Not for the first time on our journey, exasperation and impatience overcame good sense, and we lifted off with a fuel supply that was marginal in both quantity and quality. As Mick and I struggled against a stiff headwind, burning a gallon of fuel a minute, I couldn't help thinking about all those two-stroke-engine scooters in Agra and the nasty effect this rotten juice might be having on our engines.

But as our groundspeed slowed to 53 miles per hour, all I cared about was quantity. I switched to tanks one, two and four, taking care to run them all dry. All the tanks recirculate into number three, making it our last-chance tank. To say the last fifteen minutes of our flight were tense is putting it mildly.

About a mile from the airport, the starboard fuel pressure gauge started to flicker, followed by the port gauge. We still had 2,000 feet of altitude when we lost power. I thought we could glide to the edge of the runway, but tipping the nose down sloshed a bit of fuel into the engines and gave us enough power to make the asphalt. We spluttered to a relieved stop just clear of the runway.

THE LONGEST LEG

It took two hours of paper-shuffling and barking at officials to get away the next day. As so often, the difficulties we experienced

Above: Latitude 22°30'N, longitude 88°27'E
Peter takes a long drink of water in preparation for the 686-mile flight from Calcutta to Rangoon (Yangon), in Burma (Myanmar). Lang plots their course, which will first take them across the Ganges delta and over the port city of Chittagong, in Bangladesh, where, on February 13, 1919, Ross Smith, Wally Shiers and Jim Bennett had a miraculous escape aboard the steamship *Sphinx* when it exploded and sank in Chittagong harbor. The blast occurred directly under Ross's cabin, but he was on deck.

on the ground only magnified the pleasure and freedom we felt in the air. But there was another problem we had not anticipated. All our running around had left us perspiring heavily in the subcontinental heat. Having jettisoned our heavy flight suits in Bahrain to save weight, we were wearing only our thin Nomex overalls when we took off in our hot, damp state—only to find ourselves chilled to the bone after eight to ten hours' exposure to a brisk, 80-mile-per-hour breeze. What was more serious, my extremities also started to go numb, which made for a few adventurous landings.

We were getting used to handling the aircraft with the enormous fuel load of 4,500 pounds required for these long flights, but had to be very careful turning close to the ground. We crossed one of the wide sweeps of the Ganges, and droned along for hour after hour over marshy green expanses. The earth was so flooded it might well have been an ocean we were crossing. The only break in our calm came when our support planes intercepted us briefly after paying their courtesy call to the air force base at Allahabad. Over the last 100 miles, however, visibility deteriorated steadily, and as we neared Dum Dum airport, at Calcutta, we had to rely on our instruments. Although I couldn't see any distance ahead, I could see straight down to the dense housing around the city, surrounded by numerous dikes and canals.

We climbed out onto the tarmac in the searing heat, to be greeted by mounds of flowers and a gaggle of photographers. After a flight lasting ten hours and ten minutes, it was quite a strain to be sociable, but mercifully our hosts swept us off in a car after about twenty minutes. Having been to Calcutta before, I was not as shocked by the city's abject poverty as some of the other crew members were. In fact, I felt some pangs of guilt for not being more moved by the pathetic scenes all around us.

THE PLAGUE FLIES AGAIN

The question of the airborne plague was also pressing on our minds once again, now that it had grown into a worldwide media scare and more and more countries were refusing admission to airline passengers from India. We hadn't spoken openly about the problem, but we all knew we could yet be grounded. Mick Reynolds and Ian Snell decided to take matters into their own hands and to leave with the Islander and the Nomad at sunrise the next morning.

Lang, Dan and I stayed in Calcutta, as we needed a day to rest up and do some maintenance work on the Vimy. This turned out to be just as well, as rain bucketed down for five hours solid—not exactly ideal flying weather. We found out later that the crews of the support aircraft had spent three hours at the airport that morning arguing with immigration

Dr. Alexander Graham Bell, who was the president of the National Geographic Society in 1898, took this picture of Benares, the Hindu holy city situated on the banks of the sacred river Ganges.

The Vimy speeds across the dense, inhospitable mountains of northern Burma. The beautiful but distinctly unforgiving terrain stretched uninterrupted for more than five hours' flying time. Golden temples announced that the plane was now in the land of Buddha.

officials. Finally airborne, they found that their problems had only just begun. The spread of the plague was making authorities everywhere jumpy. Both aircraft were refused permission to land and refuel at Chittagong, in Bangladesh, and elected to fly direct to Rangoon (now Yangon), thinking they might have just enough fuel to get there.

Over Chittagong, they ignored repeated orders from the controllers to return to Calcutta. Mick and Ian promptly switched their radios off, feigning a reception failure. Nearing Rangoon, desperately low on fuel, they argued with the controllers. Despite initial resistance, their ploy worked, and they were allowed to land. On arrival, all the crew members were taken into quarantine, where they were examined and declared fit. But they were treated quite hospitably, and quickly released.

Today was my first chance to spend some time alone and to reflect on my expectations of the journey. I longed for more of a sense of time-travel, and had had no idea that our expedition would turn into such a social circuit of speech-making and receptions. I was, of course, flattered by the attention we had received, and I wondered if it had been the same for Ross Smith. Both of us were obliged to take on hectic public relations schedules. I certainly appreciated all the free meals, but over the last week I had lost touch with Ross, except for those wondrous moments orbiting the Taj Mahal.

BULLFIGHT IN ALLAHABAD

While we were taxi-ing to the far end, preparatory to taking off, a fine bull broke on to the ground, and as we swung round to take off he charged head on toward the machine. The position, though ridiculous, was extremely hazardous....

I frightened him for the moment by a roar from the engines. Evidently he took the roar for a challenge, and stood in front of the Vimy, pawing the ground and bellowing defiantly. At this point a boy scout rushed out from the crowd to move the monster, and, much to the amusement of ourselves and the crowd, the bull changed his intention and turned on the hero. Our brave toreador retreated to the fence, pursued by the bull.

We took advantage of the diversion and made a more hurried ascent than usual. What became of the scout I do not know, but as we circled above I noticed that the bull was still in sole possession of the aërodrome.

ROSS SMITH IN ALLAHABAD,
NOVEMBER 28, 1919

Above: The steep green hillsides of Burma offer striking beauty but little relief in the event of a forced landing. Mechanic Dan Nelson took this shot from his perch in the Vimy's nose, which gave the best view of the glory, and the danger, below.

Center: Among the most important centers of Buddhism, Rangoon has numerous temples and shrines where the religious come to pay homage to Siddhartha (one of several names by which Buddha is known), the spiritual leader of their faith.

MINOR COMPLAINTS

I was amazed that the Vimy had held up so well. The bracing wires were still taut, although the right engine seemed to be vibrating more than when we started. The gearbox temperature also seemed to be higher on the right side. Routine maintenance had been difficult on the last few legs owing to the long flights and the problems we had had getting access to airport facilities in India. The engines were losing power, but I thought it might only be because of the heat and humidity.

With a long day ahead, we got to the airport at 4 a.m. the next morning, hoping for an early start. Poking around in the darkness of the ancient control tower, Lang and I plodded through our various briefings. The building was in a pretty bad state of disrepair, and the radio equipment looked as though it had come off the set of a John Wayne war movie. No one seemed to notice our presence in the early morning hours, least of all the officials sleeping soundly in the hallway. Unusually for India, our customs clearance was fairly informal. We woke up the customs officer in his inner office, and he obligingly stamped our flight plans. His first

four inkpads proved to be bone dry, but fortunately he had a whole drawerful of them! Another time-saver was that we didn't have to get our passports stamped to leave India, since they hadn't been stamped back in Delhi owing to our having been rushed off to the Prime Minister's house.

We still had a few problems to sort out before we could leave, the most urgent being that our right outboard tire had gone flat. An airline mechanic produced a nitrogen bottle, but it had no pressure. Eventually, someone found a foot pump, and that did the job. One more task then remained before takeoff. The Vimy was parked in a depression, so it took quite a bit of work to push her out. As it was a steamy morning, we worked up a good sweat, leading to the familiar problem that we would wind up frozen after a few hours of sitting motionless in the cockpit.

As always, I was worried about taking off with a full fuel load in the extreme heat, particularly with Dan on board as well, but we staggered off the long runway with no real problem. Our initial performance was meager, but we did our best to claw our way into the clouds, climbing at only about 100 feet

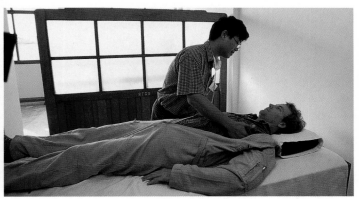

Despite official concern about the airborne plague, the Vimy crew were allowed to land in Burma, but were immediately quarantined and examined by a doctor (*below*). They were quickly released and processed through customs at Yangon Airport. "We were actually treated very well," recalled Bev Kidby. "The paperwork was a breeze compared to what we struck in other countries," said husband Lang. The entire press corps of this city of three million people turned out for the landing. Ross Smith's Vimy was the first plane ever to land here.

a minute. I had to guide the fuel-swollen aircraft very gingerly to the left to clear the higher treetops and to avoid the built-up areas east of the airport.

THE GREEN PART OF THE WORLD

With mile after mile of swamps, marshes and rice paddies, Bengal offered no more suitable spots for a forced landing than it did in 1919: *All the flat stretches along the coast were paddy-fields under water. We were wet and miserable, and the thought often-times came over me of what an ignominious end it would be if we had engine trouble and were forced to land in a paddy-field of mud and water.* (Ross Smith flying over Asia, December 1, 1919)

The early light made the earth glow green. I tried to enjoy the scenery and not to listen too hard to the engines. In a foolhardy moment, we hadn't bothered to bring our life raft, a decision we had cause to regret as we looked down on the Ganges delta to see it spread out as wide as a small ocean. Beyond that was Chittagong harbor, and I was reminded of Ross Smith's mishap here aboard the steamship *Sphinx* en route from India to Australia in 1919 to survey landing grounds for his planned flight to Australia. The ship exploded and sank with the fuel he and his crew intended to deposit at the chosen sites.

As we entered the hilly countryside of Burma (now Myanmar), the landscape turned a much darker shade of green. There were no paved roads, but we could see numerous villages clumped on the hillsides. It became almost impossible to read a map, as there was no way of distinguishing between the countless wildly irregular rivers and gorges. When flying over Burma, with its vast expanses of savage, uninhabited mountains covered with spinach-green jungle and its sharp outcrops of rock, it's hard to believe that the country has a population of 44 million. I tried to enjoy the spectacular and primitive beauty below us, but I kept thinking about the disastrous consequences of a possible engine failure—particularly for Dan, who was riding in the bow.

We would truly be on our own if any problems arose, as we were out of radio contact for hours on end. Some relief was offered by the sight of a little river valley, complete with an overgrown Japanese airstrip, but it was short-lived. On the other side of the valley, the terrain again rose steeply, and here, the tops of the hills were obscured in clouds. More than once we dived through a low spot in a ridge line and barely scraped over the trees, less than 100 feet below the clouds. The engines were a lot steadier than my nerves. Even if we were to survive a crash, I estimated that we wouldn't make more than a mile or so a day through this forbidding territory.

We steered through a few squalls, and after about six hours the terrain started to flatten out and we dropped into the basin of the Irawaddy River. About 70 miles from Rangoon, we reestablished radio contact, and shortly after dodged around a large thunderstorm that lay in our path and was lighting up the sky with some sizable bolts. One of them struck less than 100 yards off our right wing. From his seat in the crow's nest,

Above: A young boy serving tourists improvises a glass of ice water to cool off in the heat of the tropical climate. "The Buddhist religion holds that life involves great suffering," observed Nomad pilot Mick Reynolds, "but the Burmese also know how to enjoy themselves, and we were shown a very good time during our brief stay in Rangoon."

Dan turned around and looked at me, to make sure that the pilot had also seen the sparkler off to our right! We gave the storm a wide berth but still got drenched.

The golden temples of Shwedagon were clearly visible in the distance as we landed. The entire press corps of this city of three million people had turned out to meet us, but first we had to endure the indignity of being rushed into quarantine and checked for plague symptoms. A young male doctor asked me to lie down on a table and then proceeded to poke and prod at various parts of my body. I tried hard not to look sick, but how was I supposed to look after eight and a half hours with my head in the breeze? We did our usual performance at the press conference, and many of the reporters seemed surprised and impressed to learn that the Vimy had been the first aircraft ever to land here, in 1919. The officials then took us on a

quick, barefooted tour around the golden pagodas, before the sun went down.

SIAM BECKONS

We took off in the morning for Bangkok. As we crossed the Gulf of Mergui, the right engine was sounding poorly: it was definitely missing on a cylinder, although it improved with some manipulation of the throttles. We threaded through the rugged hills at Three Pagodas Pass, between Burma and Thailand, flying low over numerous unforgiving gorges to provide some exciting footage for the television crew.

Once again, there was very little hospitable terrain for a sudden stop, but I had become resigned to that risk for the time being. Jim was busily snapping photos from his perch in the nose, obviously unaware of, or unconcerned about, the danger he faced as the first person who would come into contact with the rocks

A woman prays at the Shwedagon Pagoda in Rangoon. This massive golden monument stands more than 300 feet tall and has a 76-carat diamond embedded in the tip of its vane. There has been a temple on this site for more than 2,500 years, but the present structure dates to 1769, when the temple was largely rebuilt after an earthquake.

Opposite page:
Latitude 16°45'N, longitude 96°11'E
Looking down Mahabandoola Street to the Sule Pagoda, in the center of Rangoon. The golden temple enshrines several strands of the Buddha's hair and has been rebuilt many times over the past 2,000 years, having suffered the wrath of numerous earthquakes.

Opposite page: Tree bark ground and mixed with water forms a cosmetic paste to beautify young Buddhist women.

This page: Photographer Jim Stanfield, a veteran of many missions in Burma for *National Geographic*, captured these sights of Rangoon during the day he spent there as part of the Vimy team. "Despite the political turmoil," Jim said, "the Burmese are as friendly and hospitable as any people in the world."

and timber below. We passed over a large lake not on the map. Initially, I questioned our navigation, but it simply confirmed what we already suspected, that our maps of this region were out-of-date.

Beyond the lake was a ridge of mountains, and beyond that were the watery flats of Thailand, endless miles of fish farms and rice paddies. The only memorable landmark was a giant statue of Buddha in the final stages of construction. Ever mindful of a photo opportunity, we dived steeply over the huge figure, so that Jim could get a picture.

At Bangkok, we landed beside a huge mob of press lined up along the runway and were smartly led off to meetings and interviews that proved to be painfully slow, since all questions and answers had to be translated into Thai. We were then graciously informed that we owed landing and handling fees of $2,700 to our kind hosts! Some aggressive haggling succeeded in halving this sum, but

we vowed not to accept any further invitations to land at Thailand's wallet-shrinking airports.

After three tedious hours at the airport, we arrived at our hotel in a state of extreme hunger. I led the charge on what I thought was a complimentary snack buffet in the lobby, and we started to graze enthusiastically through the field of hors d'oeuvres and pastries. After a few minutes, the Assistant Manager came rushing over to inform us we were eating someone's wedding buffet. Seriously embarrassed, we slunk away to the bar, where Mick Reynolds and I relieved our tension with some very welcome Thai brew.

On this third stage of our journey, we had conquered all the obstacles put in our way by bureaucracy, national borders and even a plague. We were tired but in a triumphant mood. We had a grand night in Bangkok, celebrating the fact that we were on the home stretch to Australia. Nothing could stop us now—as long as the props kept turning!

Latitude 18°51'N, longitude 94°39'E

The Vimy threads her way through Three Pagodas Pass, which marks the border between Burma and Thailand. The dense vegetation hides a remote but active trail for smugglers passing between the two countries. With the menacing jungle below, a mechanical problem in this region would have spelled disaster. Photographer Jim Stanfield was unfazed by his perilous perch in the exposed bow of the plane. "It was a rare privilege to see Burma as we did, from just above the treetops," he said. "It was truly spectacular."

STAGE FOUR: DREAMS

TURN TO NIGHTMARES

Stage Four:
Dreams Turn to
Nightmares

October 5 to October 9: Bangkok–Sumatra

MAYBE IT WAS LACK OF SLEEP after a night on the town in Bangkok. I hadn't got to bed until 2 a.m., and Dan Nelson and Bob Shaw had only just made it back for our 4 a.m. ride out to the airport. Maybe it was the sight of those boiling black clouds off our left wing. Or maybe I was hearing things and imagining the sound of engine trouble. Was I just losing confidence in the "old bus"? Or was I losing confidence in myself? A case of LMF, lack of moral fiber, as the British Army used to stamp the files of soldiers courtmartialed for cowardice. Whatever the reasons, I knew it was going to be a bad day.

Right: The huge limestone outcrops of Thailand's southeastern coast are a spectacular sight, but became menacing obstacles as descending rain clouds forced the Vimy to thread a path between them.

Previous page: Latitude 1°20'N, longitude 103°50'E
The Vimy glides above the Putri Narrows between Singapore and Johore Bahru, on the Malay Peninsula. Ross Smith had to land the Vimy on the tiny Singapore racecourse, which proved even more perilous on takeoff. A few tree branches came with the airplane, stuck in the wires of the undercarriage.

With our mysteriously reduced power, we had barely managed to scrape over the city's taller buildings on our departure from Bangkok. Much to the annoyance of the air traffic controllers, I had deviated from our assigned flight path, trying to keep a park or golf course within gliding range as we crossed the dense urban sprawl. And now here we were, in pelting rain, miles out over the Gulf of Thailand, out of sight of land—and without our life raft, which we had left behind in the Nomad in our haste to get away. With visibility that can best be likened to flying inside a frosted lightbulb, it was hard to decide which was worse: the threat of running smack into some unseen solid object or the possibility of disappearing without a trace into the watery gray expanses below.

After about forty-five minutes of wallowing in self-pity as we probed our way around the heaviest squalls, I suddenly sighted the coastline again. Stretched out before us lay the spectacular eastern shore of Thailand, with its broad beaches, its dense, green jungles and the stark outcrops of rock along the east coast. Then the Islander joined us for a few minutes, raising my spirits even further, but because they were getting low on fuel, they could not stay with us and had to divert to Phuket. No sooner were they out of sight than another little storm forced us down to scud along at only 200 feet above the jungle. It was the hardest rain we had flown through since Europe.

With all the changes in heading and altitude the storms had forced on us, I could not be absolutely sure about the note of the engines, but my instincts told me the right side was complaining. In an effort to detect any unusual vibrations, I clamped my hands over my earphones to shut out any extraneous noise, craned my neck to the right, felt the

Left: October 5: The lumbering aircraft, here over Chumphon, in Thailand, had difficulty plying its way around the violent storms of Southeast Asia. Unable to climb over them and too slow to fly around them, Peter and Lang were forced to "scud run" underneath and hope for sufficient clearance above the jungles and paddies.

Above: Looking down on Malaysia's Perak River. Rivers were among the few definitive landmarks identifiable at the Vimy's low altitudes.

Dancing girls of Siam (Thailand). The Smith brothers had a narrow escape in the Asian kingdom when, landing in a waterlogged, stump-studded field at Singora (Songkhla), their tailskid was wrenched off.

instrument panel with my fingertips, and performed a few other contortions. The Vimy's symptoms were mild, but she was definitely sick.

JUNGLE FEVER

We had intended to fly over Songkhla (formerly Singora), where the Smith brothers had so nearly come to grief as they came in to land in a field full of stumps, but a solid wall of clouds forced us to turn right over Surat Thani and track directly west, across the isthmus of Thailand. With some maneuvering around unkind terrain and weather, I was able to reach the west coast of the Malay Peninsula two hours later, where the hills were lower but so was the visibility. There was a small airfield at Trang, in Thailand, not far from the Malaysian border. As we passed over the little runway at 500 feet, Lang looked at me.

"You OK to go on?" he shouted into the intercom. I nodded, but registered that this was the first sign of hesitation I had ever had from Lang. Maybe he was hearing something, too.

After five and a half hours in the air, the wind, the rain and fatigue were taking their toll on both of us, but we knew that good facilities lay ahead in Penang, less than two hours due south. But a direct course would take us across the Straits of Malacca, and there was no doubt that the starboard engine was sounding progressively worse. I whistled a tune to myself, trying not to think about the possibility of plunging into the brown water below.

Left: A local food stall on the Malaysian island of Pulau Langkawi. It was the crew's good fortune to find this prosperous island and so end an agonizing flight in foul weather with an ailing right engine. The villagers here were extremely hospitable to their drop-in guests. Langkawi was home to the Vimy crew for two nights and two days of repairs and testing.

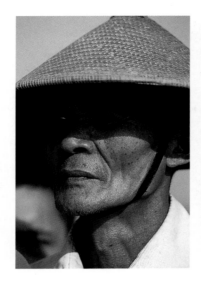

Local rice farmers came out of the paddies to watch the Vimy's engine runs and test flights. Fascinated by the plane, they seemed undisturbed by the noise of the engines roaring for hour after hour. Traditional and modern ways of life could be seen in sharp contrast in most of the Vimy's Asian ports of call, and Langkawi was no exception.

The cloud ceiling was down to 500 feet, with minimal forward visibility, when the right engine started to splutter seriously. The RPMs became unstable, and the tachometer needle was inexplicably surging back and forth. After a few moments of pulse-racing panic, I managed to pull myself together and review our options. The only thing in sight above water was a small sandbar off the left side. As we left it behind us, I shuddered at the vision of the Vimy—and the efforts of so many people—sinking irrevocably beneath the murky waves below. For a split second I mourned, and then forced myself to focus on the task at hand.

Lang figured we had lost a cylinder, most likely because of spark plug failure. "That's not so bad. She can run on seven," I said, with a confidence I was far from feeling. Fortunately, we were carrying a detailed chart for western Malaysia. Our little paper savior was somewhat tattered and sodden, but it indicated an airfield only 12 miles away, on Langkawi island. As our motor growled unhappily, I steered us 30 degrees to the right.

Langkawi appeared out of the mist, its near side offering a choice of cliffs or steep-walled jungle, without so much as a yard of beach to cushion our landing. I eased back on the control wheel to give us enough height to scrape over a fast-approaching ridge, and the other side of the island revealed a small town lying at the edge of a lagoon. With another tug, our big green box kite just made it over a second bushy ridge, beyond which we could see a large, modern airport only 4 miles ahead.

Lang made a vain attempt to explain who, what and where we were. "Say again aircraft type," the tower requested. "That's Vimy—Victor, India, Mike, Yankee," Lang repeated. But they still didn't get the picture. "Vimy, please instruct aircraft *type*." His patience starting to wear as thin as the controllers', Lang made one last try. "Langkawi, that's Vimy, Vimy, Vimy—type is Vimy." We dispensed with further formalities. Even though we were closing in on the airport, visibility was so poor the controllers couldn't see us. They instructed us to land to the northeast, the normal procedure for passenger jets. We should have requested the other runway, but we were so desperate to put an end to our miserable marathon that we accepted their instructions, despite a brisk tailwind. My approach was too sharp. With the wind behind us, I made a hideous, crow-hopping touchdown, our poor tires screeching until they must have been almost square. But we had returned to terra firma, to find ourselves in one of the nicest places on Earth at that—even though I hadn't known Langkawi existed until fifteen minutes earlier!

The old and the new coexist in close proximity in many parts of Asia. Life on Bangkok's bustling waterways, one of the major arteries of commerce, has changed little from Ross Smith's time.

Below: Dan Nelson checks the eroded spark plug that caused the unpleasant sounds coming from the right engine as the Vimy flew over western Malaysia. A motorcycle plug produced from the bottom of a dealer's box on Langkawi island was made to do duty, shortened by the addition of three washers.

Right: The biplane breaks ground for a test hop around Langkawi. Although its performance was improved, the right engine was still down on power. There was no choice but to push on to Singapore, where the maintenance facilities would be better. Far from being solved, the problems were just beginning.

Lang attended to immigration details while I started pulling off the side panels to inspect our ailing powerplant. Within minutes, a curious crowd of fifty or so people had gathered around the aircraft, and I did my best to answer their questions graciously while twisting out dozens of screws to get at the patient's guts, my brittle nerves causing me to drop every third or fourth screw.

Blustery storms kept passing through, but an instructor at the local flight school, a young man named Aidi, allowed us to tie the Vimy to a sturdy fence next to the school's hangars. Meanwhile, the control tower had sent word of our whereabouts back to Phuket, in Thailand, where the Nomad and the Islander were refueling.

SCAVENGER HUNT

An hour later, Dan climbed out of the Nomad, spark plug wrench in hand, and immediately set to work on the inside bank of cylinders, while I inspected the outside. A few grunts later, he leaned toward me under the cowl and said calmly, "Check this out." He handed me the pitiful remains of a spark plug, with the electrode almost completely burned off. "That's what we needed to know," I replied. It was a relief to find the problem could be so simply remedied. But how come the plug had wound up looking like an ancient clay relic? The nasty scooter juice from Agra? Not likely, I thought; that was twenty-nine flying hours ago.

We were stuck, but the good news was that we had come down in the right place. The owner of the flight and maintenance school owned just about everything else on the island as well, including a nice motel. Having installed ourselves in his bungalows, we sat down to an excellent meal in a roofed but open-sided restaurant in the midst of a torrential downpour. The bad news was that Ian Snell was showing signs of a serious stomach ailment, which no amount of medicine or good cheer seemed to help.

There was certainly no shortage of cars and trucks on the island, but finding a Chevy spark plug (which is smaller in diameter than most) proved to be a real challenge. Dan and I went to several spare parts kiosks the next day, and got the same response each time we held up our fizzled remnant: a few words in Malay and a discouraging shake of the head. In desperation, we then drove around the island with Aidi looking for any General Motors vehicle at all, with the intention of bartering for a plug or even "borrowing" one from under someone's hood. But it soon became clear that the world's largest auto manufacturer had yet to discover Langkawi. Before contacting Kuala Lumpur for help, we decided to try

Latitude 6°16'N, longitude 99°48'E

Red sky at night, sailor's delight. Not so for airmen, unfortunately. The glowing atmosphere warns of smoke from Malaysia's burning jungles, which would plague the Vimy crew for several days. Engine problems would make for some exciting moments as well. Flying over parts of Southeast Asia became an exercise in suspense.

one more kiosk. The vendor rummaged through a few boxes and produced a motorcycle plug that was the right diameter but about half an inch too long. Dan immediately saw that we could use it if we added a few washers to the rim to shorten the shaft.

Returning to the airfield for a test flight, we found it swarming with jets, jeeps and paratroopers, one of whom landed on the tail of the Nomad. Fortunately, it was only a military exercise. When the smoke had cleared, about an hour later, the field was still held by the good guys, and we took the Vimy up. Dan flew beside me in the copilot's seat, and we agreed she was nowhere near as good as new. Back on the ground, we pulled off the air cleaners, and then took her up again. The improvement was only marginal, but we thought she would be good enough to make it to Singapore, where we could give her a thorough going-over. At least Jim Stanfield, going up in a small plane with Aidi, had scored some spectacular aerial shots as the sun set over this magnificent tropical island.

A primitive mill for pressing coconuts and extracting their oil. Coconuts were a vital source of fluid for Ross Smith and crew in parts of Asia where the quality of drinking water was unreliable.

 Right: Latitude 4°14'N, longitude 100°48'E
"Mate, where's the nearest airfield?" The answer to Lang's question was an abandoned World War II Japanese strip at Sitiawan, in Malaysia. Vibrations from the right engine made it imperative to find a place to land promptly. The Nomad swoops overhead to make sure the Vimy arrived without incident on the overgrown aerodrome.

Above and far right: A local school was let out to give the kids a closer look at the Vimy during her unscheduled stop at Sitiawan. Much to their delight, the youngsters were almost blown over backwards by the prop blast from the Vimy's engines. The starboard engine seemed to stabilize after the pilots reset the fuel injection computer.

ANOTHER "PRECAUTIONARY" LANDING

The following morning, October 6, we made Penang without incident and then took off on the next leg, to Kuala Lumpur. Lang was in the pilot's seat. At about 11:30 a.m. local time, he turned to me and said calmly, "Mate, where's the nearest airfield?" From him, those were serious words. I hadn't detected any change in the engine noise, but Lang pointed to the right tachometer needle, which was dipping badly. We were crossing a bay at 2,200 feet and barely in gliding range of shore.

My fumbling fingers went racing over the map. A small circle within an X on the chart marked a closed airstrip at the town of Sitiawan, 9 miles behind us. By the time I had reset the

navigational system to show us the way—after first switching it off in my nervous haste—we were practically over the top of the lush grass strip. Lang brought us around in a continuing left turn. It looked as though no one had used the field since the Japanese had abandoned it back in World War II, but the knee-high grass made a nice landing cushion.

Mick and Ian followed us in, in the two support craft. Within minutes, a mob of little schoolkids had appeared from nowhere. It was as if the circus had just come to town. After some discussion, I suggested we check the injection computers before we started ripping things apart. One of the computers for the right engine turned out to have been wrongly set,

Malay children in Singapore, where the Vimy touched down in 1919. The landing ground was so small that Jim Bennett had to crawl along the fuselage and apply his weight to the tail to help stop the plane.

allowing insufficient fuel through the intake system. We reset it to match the left side and then ran up the power, much to the delight of the youngsters, who were practically blown end over end by the prop wash. Everything seemed OK, so Lang turned the nose into the wind and our big bird slowly gathered speed, mowing a path through the long grass.

Barely airborne, we had to steer around the taller of the palm trees at the far end of the strip, and I held my breath, as if that would help lift us up, until we had put a reasonable margin between us and the dense web of a palm grove that lay just beyond the airstrip. As we circled to gain height, I kept an anxious eye on the two planes below,

knowing that takeoff would be more treacherous for them, with their higher liftoff speeds and the difficulty their smaller tires would have beating a path through the tall grass. Mick practically climbed the Nomad up the first tree at the end of the strip. Ian or Mark, whoever had the wheel of the Islander, cleared a little more easily.

We elected to bypass Kuala Lumpur and go straight to Singapore owing to the dense layer of smoke that enveloped central Malaysia from seasonal burning that had got out of control. This restricted landings to aircraft with substantially more instruments than we had. After the first hour, the right engine started acting up again, but it seemed to settle down

The Vimy patrols above Singapore's broad harbor. The modern city-state was home for two days of pageantry, with a bit of maintenance thrown in. Peter and Mick Reynolds flew the plane around the island on October 8 after she was treated to sixteen new spark plugs. The Vimy sounded as good as new…for now.

each time we passed over an airfield: first Port Dickson, then Melacca, then Johore Bahru. In between, we passed over nothing at all inviting in the event of an emergency landing—just miles of deep, green rubber plantations, which later gave way to mangrove swamps. It took four nail-biting hours to reach the haven of Singapore, but here we were rewarded with the magnificent sight of a huge red and white marquee erected by the local Shell folks for our arrival party at Singapore's Seletar Airport.

DANCING LIONS
Singapore turned on a truly splendid reception for us, with Chinese lion dancers, cymbal bands, and lots of speeches and photos. I nodded

and applauded through the speeches, but in fact I was quite deaf from having removed my headset during much of the flight in an effort to detect even the slightest change in the engine note.

At the close of the day, we put our machine to bed in a large, gloomy prewar hangar, where the only light came leaking through large-caliber bullet holes in the heavy steel doors—a grim reminder of the dark days of 1942, when the city fell to the Japanese.

The next morning, Ian Snell and I went down to breakfast together, but he had to leave abruptly, feeling poorly again. Dan and I then set off for Seletar Airport, where we found a huge crowd had gathered

Above: The Vimy's shadow pulls alongside in close formation as she makes her final approach into Singapore's Seletar Airport. A gala reception awaits the crew after another nail-biting day nursing a sick right-side engine over the dense jungles and rubber plantations of Southeast Asia.

A traveling restaurant in Singapore. Ross Smith and crew made a two-day stopover here to catch up on much-needed meals and rest.

around our hangar, obliging us to postpone our maintenance tasks until after we had rolled the Vimy out for a public viewing. Eventually, Dan set about changing the oil, while I literally monkeyed about in the flying wires, contorting myself into all kinds of positions to remove the grime and rust accumulated since the wings were first strung together in California. We perked up remarkably when Kevin Treloar, from Hawker-Pacific's maintenance operation, appeared on the scene with a brand-new set of Chevy spark plugs.

A TRAGIC LOSS

But our good cheer wasn't to last long. Not long after we had installed the new plugs, Mark Rebholz arrived with the news that Ian had been rushed to the hospital in excruciating pain with what appeared to be a kidney stone. The expedition

"THANK YOU, SIR. WHAT DID HE SAY?"
I regretted that I was quite unable to reply to their kindly expressions, as I did not hear them. The roar of the exhausts for nine consecutive hours' flying had affected my ears so that I was quite deaf.

ROSS SMITH ON LANDING IN DELHI,
NOVEMBER 25, 1919

was over for our British friend, whose skills and good humor had contributed so much to the team. At least we knew he was in good hands until arrangements could be made to send him home.

Late that afternoon, I took the helm for a test flight with Lang, with Joe Stancampiano riding in back. Jim Stanfield had gone out in a small plane with a member of the Singapore Flying Club to get some air-to-air shots of the Vimy with the city in the background. Just as we left the ground, the fuel pressure dropped dramatically. I chopped the power, using the remaining runway to pull us up. As we coasted to a stop, it struck me that, for the first time during a mishap, I had had no sense of fear or panic.

We bled the air out of the fuel system, put more gas in, and tried again. This time, Mick replaced Lang, but Joe decided to give it a miss, still being a bit shaken from our hastily aborted takeoff. For the first time in days, we developed full power, and as the sun dipped into the sea, we looked down on a magnificently gilded cityscape. We could even pick out the tiny racetrack where Ross Smith had landed the very first plane here in Singapore.

That night, the Singapore Flying Club threw a raging party in our honor, but feeling anxious about Ian, Chris Weber and I slipped away early to pay him a visit in hospital. He was comfortable, thanks to strong painkillers, and introduced me over the phone to Malcolm Wood, the pilot who was coming out from England to replace him in two days' time. Without a British pilot, the Islander was grounded, but Malcolm would earn his stripes soon enough.

The Beginning of the End

Sunday morning was very disorganized. We had decided to push on with the Nomad, leaving the Islander to catch up with us, as we hoped, in Jakarta. We spent more than an hour packing and repacking our gear in an effort to distribute it between the two planes. Even though we jettisoned virtually all our clothes and tools, leaving them for Malcolm and Mark to bring out in the Islander in three or four days' time, the Vimy and the Nomad were bulging at the seams.

The weather was unusually clear as Jim, Dan, Lang and I taxied out in the Vimy. We took off to the north, our heavy load obliging us to circle over the airport several times to gain height. The engines certainly sounded better with the new spark plugs in place. We fought our way to 1,500 feet and headed out on a course of 175 degrees, passing over the top of Changi Airport, near the site of the infamous wartime POW camp. Soon we found ourselves over the blue expanse of the Java Sea. An hour later, we sent up a cheer as the longitude indicator flashed zeroes all the way across the dial—deeply conscious that Ross Smith's Vimy had been the first aircraft ever to cross the equator.

Nightmare Flight

We plodded along southward, sighting the occasional island, and descended to 2,000 feet in an effort to stay below the clouds. As the cloud masses thickened around us, we were forced to seek a path between their towering walls, having no chance of going over or under them. Eventually, we were so far off track that we had no choice but to navigate by

Far left: The Shell reception in Singapore had waiters in period flying gear…almost. The young man is actually wearing welder's goggles.

Left: This shot from the Nomad at 10,000 feet reveals the amoeba-like shapes of the archipelago between the southern Malay Peninsula and northern Sumatra.

Below: The Vimy says farewell to the metropolis of Singapore, but it is the ailing biplane that needs good wishes.

instruments and push blindly on. Not only could we not see the ground, we could barely see the tail of the airplane! I kept checking the map to ensure there were no volcanoes looming in wait, and was greatly relieved to find that most of the Sumatran highlands were further to the south.

I tried to steer the plane towards the brighter patches in the clouds, but the windscreen kept misting over and it was difficult to see anything at all. Even the wooden steering wheel was soaking wet from all the moisture in the atmosphere.

I am far from adept at this sort of flying, having had little instrument training, but it didn't take long to realize that I needed to keep my eyes glued to the compass and the attitude indicator. Even a momentary loss of equilibrium can cause the aircraft to bank or dive suddenly, and this can quickly deteriorate into an unrecoverable spin, since the pilot no longer has any natural orientation to show which way is up, down, left or right. After about two hours of these exhausting conditions, we determined our position and began a descent in an attempt to establish visual contact with the ground. We sure hoped to make visual before physical contact!

I pushed the nose down slightly and tried to hold a constant rate of descent of about 100 feet per minute. A pilot would usually do this by maintaining a slightly higher airspeed than normal, but our airspeed indicator was no use, being permanently stuck on 40 miles per hour. The only way I could keep a steady rate of descent was by the feel of the breeze on my face. When the breeze got too strong, I would ease back on the control wheel and then glance at the altimeter to cross-check our descent.

We leveled out at 1,000 feet, still unable to see in any direction, but we did notice that the damp, clammy feeling we had been experiencing for the last two hours had gone. I was just becoming aware of a strong smell of burning when Lang turned to me and said, "These aren't clouds, mate. We're in smoke!" Gingerly, I let the Vimy down a little bit more, and at about 600 feet, I could begin to make out the jungle immediately below. We couldn't see very far, but everything we could see was on fire, and we were caught in the thick of a huge pall of smoke.

For about forty nerve-racking minutes, we managed to scud along at 100 feet or so above the treetops. The forward visibility was only about a mile, giving us less than a minute to avoid any obstacle that might suddenly appear in our path. This required all my concentration, and I didn't dare look to the sides, where the engine gauges were mounted. At one point, to alert me to a drop in the fuel pressure gauge, indicating that we needed to change tanks, the resourceful Dan jiggled the rudder cables running along the outside of the fuselage, making the pedals vibrate under my feet. I didn't see the airfield at Palembang until we were right over the top of it, and lost sight of it again as I turned away to set up for landing. Steering back on course with the aid of the compass, I was surprised at how relaxed the control tower operators sounded, given the horrendous conditions. We landed with a thump—a sure sign that a pilot is anxious.

That flight of three hours and fifty-five minutes was worse than anything I had ever experienced. Lang could see how shaken I was and tried to cheer me up, but I just sat in the

Latitude 0°00',
longitude 104°16'E
Lang checks the map as Peter
guides the open-top aircraft across
the equator. The modern Vimy
reenacts another milestone: on
December 6, 1919, G-EAOU was the
first plane ever to cross the equator.

LIFE IN THE BALANCE

*The moment one plunges into heavy cloud there is
misty blankness; all objects are lost to view; and as
time wears on, a helpless feeling grows upon one that
all sense of direction is lost....*

*At first all went well; but, while turning to check over
an engine, I apparently and unconsciously, with the
natural movement of my body, pushed one foot, which
was on the rudder bar, slightly forward. This turned
the machine off its course, and when next I looked at
my compass I was ten degrees off course. I then kicked
on the opposite rudder to bring the machine back...
[but found] I had put on too much rudder....*

*In my attempt to correct the course and bring the
needle back on to its correct reading, I glanced at the
air-speed indicator and found it registering over one
hundred miles an hour—twenty-five miles above
normal flying speed....we were flying at an inclined
angle of forty degrees.*

*I realized that the machine was slipping sideways,
and that if I did not get matters righted at once, the
machine would get out of control and go spinning
down to earth....*

*It is useless attempting to describe how I acted. A pilot
does things instinctively, and presently my instruments
told me that we were once more on our course and on
an even keel.*

*All this took but a few seconds; but they were anxious
moments, as a single mistake or the losing of one's
head would have been fatal. This happened several
times, and at the end of what seemed hours I glanced
at my watch and found we had only been in the
clouds for twelve minutes!*

ROSS SMITH EN ROUTE FROM RANGOON (NOW
YANGON) TO BANGKOK, DECEMBER 1, 1919

Above: Eyes stinging after three hours plowing through dense smoke, the pilots make a fuel stop in Palembang, Sumatra. The primitive island was enveloped from end to end in smoke from jungle clearing and routine agricultural burning at the end of the dry season. "We had to descend blindly, and didn't make visual contact with the ground until we were only a few hundred feet above the trees," said Peter.

cockpit, staring in stunned disbelief at the calluses raised on my hands from the death-grip I'd had on the wheel for the past four hours. After a few minutes, we climbed out of the plane, to be almost overwhelmed by the smell of burning. To judge by the looks on their faces, the customs officials who came out to meet us were quite taken aback by the overgrown box kite that had dropped in on them. They told us that much of the island had been burning for weeks—a routine matter of slash-and-burn forest clearance combined with burning off the fields and paddies at the end of the dry season in preparation for replanting. This obviously accounted for the controllers' nonchalance.

As the passport officer had taken the day off, another blue-shirted official had to take our documents to town by scooter. While Lang ran around attending to the formalities, Dan and I refueled the aircraft. Jim Stanfield headed straight for the terminal, returning with cookies and bottled water. Exhausted, I then snuck in a quick nap on the lower wing, while Dan climbed about in the wires tightening the bolts that hold the wooden spars in place. We had been on the ground for almost three hours when our passports were finally scootered back to us. There was no way we were going to make the arrival celebrations in Jakarta on time.

We took off, vowing not to lose sight of the ground again. My nerves wouldn't have stood a repeat performance. I kept expecting the visibility to improve, but it never did. It seemed unbelievable that virtually the whole island could be on fire.

At a height of only 400 feet, we began to lose contact with the ground in the dense smoke and haze. The right engine was also starting to run rough, and I was acutely aware that if it should fail, we would have only a few moments to negotiate a terrible crash into the burning mangrove trees below.

RIGHT GOES WRONG

When I first heard the noise from the starboard side, I hoped it was just my jangled nerves. But, glancing down, I could see that the RPMs were unstable and the tachometer needle was again fluttering back and forth. Lang just nodded when I alerted him to this ominous sign. The exhaust gas temperature had also shot up to an alarming 1,400 degrees. "Maybe it's just smoke ingestion," I told myself, with about as much conviction as a fool whistling through a graveyard. Our forward view was still little more than a mile, and with a strong wind blowing from the left, off the Java Sea, I turned us that way toward

Flying in dense smoke over Sumatra, Peter's eyes are glued to the attitude indicator on the instrument panel, the only means for him to maintain control of the aircraft. Even a momentary lapse of concentration could result in vertigo and a terminal spin. Lang (left) and Dan (in the rear cockpit) strain to make visual contact with the ground through the murky atmosphere. "I kept a pretty good grip on the wheel for those four hours," Peter said. "If she had got away from me, I wasn't too sure about getting her back. Visual disorientation can happen in the time it takes to scratch your nose."

clearer air. This played havoc with our groundspeed, but allowed us to gain the insurance of another thousand feet between ourselves and the ground.

The nasty vibrations coming from the right engine were increasing in frequency, and my anxiety was growing apace. I was constantly on the lookout for any site where we could make a forced landing. At 3:12 p.m. local time, our uncertainty was over. The right engine gave up the ghost, not with a bang but a whimper, and I watched in disbelief as the tachometer wound back to zero. Lang tried flipping a few switches, but it took no more than a moment to realize that this was futile. Some one-syllable words came to mind and mouth.

As the right propeller windmilled to a stop, the plane became hard to control with its overpowering pull to the right. I experimented with different airspeeds, but the best I could do was to hold her at about 55 miles per hour, which reduced our rate of descent to about 150 feet per minute.

We had already lost 500 feet of altitude in our initial flurry. We would hit the ground in about six minutes. This was it—we were really going to crash.

"Mayday, Mayday, Mayday. Vimy One, Vimy One, Vimy One. We've had an engine failure," Lang called into the radio. "We're making an emergency landing."

Jim was hopping about in the nose compartment, taking pictures with his Widelux camera. He seemed particularly fascinated by the image of one propeller turning while the other one was stopped cold. "Jim, not now!" I shouted. "We're about to crash!" He disappeared.

I craned my neck over the side, looking for the best alternative, but nothing looked promising. I turned to Lang.

"See any place to land?" I yelled.

"There's a small airfield about twenty-five miles away," Lang said, scanning a map.

"We'll never make it."

Above: The Vimy plows on through the dense pall over Sumatra, her starboard engine warbling with uncertainty. Peter gingerly turns the plane to the east (his left), attempting to find clearer air near the coast of the Java Sea. They must be able to see the ground if they are to survive an emergency landing.

Right, top: Disaster strikes. The right prop windmills to a stop. The plane is going down. The view below is uninviting, but at least they have cleared the worst of the smoke.

Right, below: "You OK?" Dan yells from the back seat. The left engine is still running to save the battery.

"What about that road on the left?" he said, pointing to a dirt track cutting through a paddy field.

Turning left was extremely difficult against the torque of the remaining engine, and our rate of descent increased to 300 feet per minute. I could see that the road was narrow and directly across the 20-mile-per-hour wind. As if that weren't enough, a large blue truck stood in the middle of the road, too close to land in front of, too far away to glide over. Four or five boys on bicycles dived headfirst into the deep ditches along the roadside as they saw us bearing down on them. Jim popped up one more time with his camera, and I yelled at him to get his belts on.

"We can't use the road," I shouted, seconds before touching down. With less than 50 feet to go, I added a burst of power to the left engine, which slewed the aircraft just to the right of the road. I fought to level the wings and keep us from stalling. Barely clearing a grass hut, we pancaked down into a smoldering paddy field.

Our actual touchdown was not too harsh, but seconds later we struck a 2-foot-high earthen ridge dividing this paddy from the next. A violent shock was sustained by our outer left main wheel. Then, in quick succession, we struck several more ridges, only 20 yards apart. I struggled to keep the tail down each time we were tossed into the air, to stop us pole-vaulting over the nose-skid onto our back.

"Hit the brakes, hit the brakes. We've got to stop this thing!" Lang shouted.

We smashed through three more earthen walls, and skidded to a halt in the waist-high grass.

I was stunned. Lang stayed on the radio, and Dan warned us that the field we were in was still smoldering. Another field only 50 yards to our right was engulfed in flames. I started to shut down the left engine, but Lang reminded me to leave it on to provide power for the radio. "You OK?" Dan shouted, as he scrambled forward from the aft cockpit. I nodded, pulling off my belts and life vest. "What happened?" Dan asked. "The engine just quit," I said. "She's as dead as a mackerel."

WELCOME TO SUMATRA

The area had looked sparsely inhabited from the air, but even before we could climb out of the plane, we were completely surrounded by Sumatran field workers wearing conical bamboo hats and carrying long, curved knives. I slid down the turtledeck, somewhat in awe of the hundred or so locals who were curiously drumming, thumping or poking every part of the airplane. A few were even strumming the control cables

183

A minute after the violent forced landing, Lang continues to make distress calls on the radio, while Peter and Dan check the damage. The axle support arms were twisted and broken, and the tailwheel strut was folded in half. Fires were smoldering in the recently burned-off field, but the greater danger was still approaching. The field workers, initially frightened by the huge beast dropping from the sky, surged forward and began poking and prodding the plane with a tool in one hand and, more often than not, a cigarette in the other. The first of hundreds has just arrived, walking around the right wingtip, knife in hand.

along the fuselage, as if the Vimy were a giant guitar. Seeing some of them smoking, I jumped down to push them back, but decided to do so gently, given their shiny tools.

Amidst all the confusion, the only one who really knew what to do was Jim, who had started snapping away at the mystified crowd almost the moment he climbed out of the plane. As he radioed for help, Lang handed me down the emergency beacon. I pushed through the crowd to set it up and activate it about 50 yards from the airplane, only to find that it jammed his distress calls. I then had to fight my way back through the crowd to shut it off.

Lang had managed to make contact with a Malaysian airliner, and while he was informing them of our situation, I inspected the damage to our undercarriage. A few of the support arms were twisted and broken, as was the tailwheel strut. The eighteen bungee cords that act as shock absorbers for the axles had snapped on impact with the paddy walls. Then Dan pulled out the oil dipstick. "Hey!" he cried in shock. "The case is full of water!" This was devastating news. It meant that the engine block had been punctured by a piece of stray metal. I had been hoping that the fault might prove to be nothing more than a small electrical part—but swamped, our motor would roar no more.

With a sinking heart, I stood on the wing and watched the oily water drip down from the engine onto the green fabric. A teenage boy, the only person in the swelling audience who spoke some English, looked up at me and asked, "Mister, why have you come here?"

I stared at him, at a loss for words, as I reflected on the absurdity of our situation. Where to start? "We had a problem, had to land," I finally said, adding, after another long pause, "Where is *here*?"

Above: The scene less than ten minutes after the crash landing. "I had to try to get them away from the plane," said Dan (in flying suit). "I just walked away, and most of them followed." Few of the farmers on the remote island had ever seen an airplane or a man with a full beard. "The kids were amazed, and slightly afraid of me," recalled the mechanic.

Right: A grim look from one of the locals. "They seemed friendly, but it was impossible to communicate," said Peter. "Only one young boy could speak English."

Teeming crowds came to stare at the Vimy when she landed in Indonesia in December 1919. Ross Smith took this photograph at Bima, on the island of Sumbawa.

STAGE FIVE:
THE PHOENIX RISES

STAGE FIVE:
THE PHOENIX RISES

OCTOBER 9 TO OCTOBER 22: SUMATRA–DARWIN

ERE WAS JUST A POINT on the map, 4°41'S, 105°48'E—virtually indistinguishable from the millions of other points on the globe of which most of us live our lives in blissful ignorance. But now this point was different. It was possibly the final resting place of all our dreams and hopes of the last two years. The irony of the situation was uncanny: the Smith brothers had been grounded only a few hundred miles from here. But resourcefulness overcame adversity back in 1919, and they built their own runway to escape. We would have to do the same.

Right: The giant biplane instantly became the largest tourist attraction in Sumatra, and was the first aircraft most of the locals had ever seen. The crash site developed into a frantic one-ring circus, complete with vendors and food stalls. Although swelling crowds stirred up great clouds of dust and ash, they also helped to trample the burned stubble field to a usable state for takeoff.

Previous page: Latitude 4°41'S, longitude 105°48'E
Liftoff from Sumatra. The Vimy makes her escape after a lengthy and unscheduled layover on the remote Indonesian island.

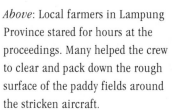

Above: Local farmers in Lampung Province stared for hours at the proceedings. Many helped the crew to clear and pack down the rough surface of the paddy fields around the stricken aircraft.

We had fetched up in a place called Cabang, a village near the end of a dirt road in Lampung Province, on the island of Sumatra. We were 140 miles short of our destination, Jakarta. This information came from our young friend Heno, who was half-Chinese and spoke broken English. I gestured to him that we needed a phone. "Mister, phone is far," he said. "How far?" I asked. "Far, far," he replied, shaking his head. "Three o'clock."

A RIDE TO DESPAIR AND BACK

It was now 3:40 p.m., and I couldn't make any sense of what he said. Nonetheless, I followed him into a small truck belonging to a road worker, and, with the three of us squeezed into the tiny cabin, we barreled off along the dirt road, scattering the oncoming mobs. In less than an hour, we had become the biggest tourist attraction in Sumatra. A little way down the road, Heno asked the driver to stop and, in an act of mercy, bought me some bottled water. I was desperately parched and had no rupiahs—and even the mighty US dollar was worthless in this little outpost of civilization.

I sat dazed in my corner as the clapped-out vehicle shuddered its way over the deeply rutted road surface.

Whenever we slowed to avoid an obstacle on the one-and-a-quarter-lane roadway, I would rouse myself, thinking we must be getting close to where the phone was. After an hour of this, the sun was starting to go down, and again I asked Heno, "How far?" He did some quick math and said, "Still much far. Two o'clock." I understood what he meant now. I could barely endure the thought of sitting in this truck for another two hours.

Heno tried to converse with me, but every word was a struggle. In any case, I preferred to be left alone to wallow in my misery. In many ways, I considered our situation to be a tragedy just slightly better than death: no tools, no parts, no support, no food, no money, no airstrip, no hope. Not to mention the suffocating and ever-present stench of burning jungle. My life savings had gone down the drain on a ridiculous, ill-fated endeavor that, at this stage of events, I doubted I could have explained to someone who spoke perfect English, let alone a few words of broken English.

I even wondered why I was bothering to make this torturous trek to a phone. Whom was I going to call, and how? I didn't have an Indonesian dime to my name, and these poor folks probably had little more. Besides, when and if I ever did get back to the Vimy, she would probably have been reduced

190

to a charred wreck as a result of one of the unruly mob of onlookers stubbing his clove cigarette out on the fabric wing.

I felt a sense of despair and futility as never before. Even when we got to the phone, in the village of Metro, I didn't achieve much. Miraculously, my phone card worked, and I got a few calls through to the Jakarta Hilton, but the other crews hadn't yet checked in. They were probably still waiting for us at Halim Airport. I also tried to call Tessa Barroll in London and my brother, Tom, in California, but everyone seemed to be gone for the weekend. My card number then quit working, as some wily computer in a distant corner of the world decided to terminate this suspicious string of calls.

Returning to the plane, I was surprised to see that the traffic—vehicle, animal and human—was just as heavy at this late hour as it had been earlier in the day. It was a harrowing experience as we went speeding along the dusty road in the dark, since our headlights were so dim we had only a few seconds to avoid any oncoming object. I found myself longing for the safety of a Calcutta taxi! But the immediate perils facing us helped me to get things in better perspective. Semidelirious after five hours in this wretched truck on this stinking island, I became resigned to my fate and resolved to do the best I could, taking one problem at a time.

Above, center: Some farmers even supplied oxen to level the field and pull out some of the larger tree stumps. The work was slow and hot, but the largest obstacles were removed just in two days.

Above: Clean water was a scarce commodity in this low-lying area at the end of the dry season. Copious quantities of boiled water were brought in for the crew by concerned local officials.

Seeing my depression, little Heno turned to me and handed me the St. Christopher medal from around his neck, saying, "Here, Mister Peter, maybe this will help you." Such a touching gesture from a boy with no shoes made me realize that we had, in fact, been blessed with extremely good fortune. We were completely unhurt and had come down amongst friendly people. Had the engine failed only a few minutes earlier, we would have crashed into dense jungle, with Jim up in the nose as the first soft object to feel the hideous impact. And what about the 3,000 pounds of fuel in our tanks? We might all have been incinerated. Or what if we had flown direct from Singapore to Jakarta? We would now, at best, be bobbing up and down as shark bait in the blue expanses of the Java Sea. Screeching around in this little wagon in the Sumatran darkness, I realized, was really as good a time as a fellow could have.

We arrived back at the crash site at 11:15 p.m. to find a few hundred curious bystanders still

Above: The grounded pilot is bone-weary after a frustrating day. "One day of rain would have trapped us in a terminal quagmire," said Peter.

Left: Mothers with babies shield themselves from the equatorial sun, but at any moment the monsoon rains, already three weeks late, could start.

on hand. I stumbled through the brush and plowed my way through the crowd toward a light by the tail. A group of uniformed soldiers was seated around a little table with a kerosene lantern, and to my great relief, I saw that the plane had been roped off from the mob. One of the soldiers handed me a note from Lang that said the rest of the crew had been taken to a local official's house. A heated discussion broke out amongst the soldiers, and I was then led to another truck, and away we went into the night.

LAMPUNG HILTON

I had some difficulty determining the hierarchy among my escorts, who were dressed in several different-colored uniforms. Along the way, we ran into a few roadblocks, and each time we stopped, there was a shouting match between the different colors, followed by a change of personnel in the open back of the truck. When we finally reached the house, about forty-five minutes after leaving the crash site, we found that the crew had gone. The official, Mr. Hidayatullah, I was

Ross Smith's article in *National Geographic* included several photographs of the Batak people of Sumatra. This remote island was the setting for Joseph Conrad's novel *Lord Jim*.

Above: Lang clears debris from the takeoff end of the would-be airstrip. "By the end of the second day, October the tenth," he recalled, "we had the strip marked out and seventy percent of it cleared of the major obstacles. It was amazing that we didn't hit one of these jagged little stumps on landing. We'd have blown a tire and wiped out the plane as it cartwheeled."

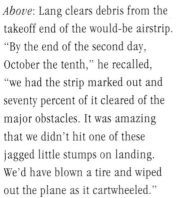

told, had taken Lang, Dan and Jim to see the commandant of Lampung Province. The soldiers motioned that I should get cleaned up, as I, too, was about to be taken to an audience with the "big boss". "How far?" I ventured to ask Heno. "Far, far," was the predictable reply. Then came the clincher: "Commandant is in Metro, next to phone."

We had been back on the road for nearly an hour when we swerved to avoid an oncoming jeep and slid to a halt about 100 yards further on. We backed up to the jeep, and I saw my comrades sprawled out in the back, all fast asleep. They were being driven back to Mr. H's house, having just come from Metro. After a high-decibel discussion amongst my military escorts, I was allowed to join them and to skip the expedition to the commandant's. I woke up Dan, who gave me the rundown on their interrogation by the commandant (whose wife had had to act as interpreter). He also had a few stories to relate of how terrified the other officers had been in the presence of the

"big boss". Dan referred to our local host, Mr. Hidayatullah, as "the Major", but that was just a guess at his rank. As the jeep trundled back toward the Major's house, Dan told me the most important news of all: the Nomad had come over the crash site at sunset, so Mick Reynolds knew the score.

When we finally made it back to the Major's house at 2:30 a.m., we were all fatigued to the point of stupor. I fell asleep instantly on a vinyl sofa, despite getting stuck to it in the unrelenting heat. An hour later, I was awakened by a loud banging at the door. It was a bunch of local journalists, who had tracked us down in the middle of the night. All I remember after that is seeing the four of them spread on the floor fast asleep the next morning.

SUMATRAN SAPPERS

The Major and his extensive entourage fed us well, and then took us back to the Vimy. I was feeling greatly buoyed by the

Left: Food stalls were quickly set up by enterprising Lampung locals, who took advantage of abandoned huts next to the aircraft. The crew retained a vivid memory of one persistent pedlar, equipped with a cooler on wheels, who nearly drove them mad by honking his bicycle horn for hours on end! Local officials fed the crew bread and butter with chocolate sprinkles—promptly dubbed "maggot sandwiches".

Above: The 1st Royal Changkuliers Brigade in action with their tool of choice, a type of one-piece spade called a *changkul*. Hours of backbreaking labor went into hacking down the 2-foot-high walls between the rice paddies. Fortunately, the fields had never been flooded, or the walls would have been higher. The field was a matrix of squares about 25 yards across.

news about Mick—the cavalry was on the way, armed with a new motor. But for now, we were left to our own meager devices to build a strip and pull off the dead powerplant.

On Monday, October 10, Dan and I spent a frustrating day dismantling first the cowling and then the engine accessories with our pitiful set of hand tools, breaking several wrenches as we struggled to remove the bolts, which had stuck hard. It took six hours to accomplish what could have been done in one in a normal workshop. Meanwhile, Lang marked out an area of about 300 yards by 20 yards for our improvised airfield. With the Major's help, he then hired a few dozen of the local field workers to begin the laborious process of pulling out tree stumps and hacking down the earth walls (or "bunds") between the paddies. The somewhat ragged-looking crew was hired at the rate of about $1.50 per man a day, and most came equipped with their tool of choice, a type of one-piece, long-handled spade called a *changkul*.

A Batak hut on Sumatra. On reaching the Sumatran coast in 1919, the Vimy fell into *an immense vacuum...[as it] bumped across the line [equator] into the Southern Hemisphere*.

Above: Having largely exhausted their manpower and animal power, Peter and Lang finished the runway on the third day with the help of a decrepit earthmover. One of the treads was sticking, so, to keep the machine from tracking around in circles, Lang had to use a shovel like a giant crutch to pivot it back on course. Building runways is dirty work in this part of the world.

Above, right: At 1740 hours on October 11, Major Mick Reynolds christened the newly carved-out airstrip amidst a huge dust storm. Touching down, the Nomad's tires began to bog in the spongy soil. He quickly brought up the throttles, and even more dust, but only his fast action gave the plane enough momentum to plow its way to the north end and give the advancing Islander a clear path.

The 1st Royal Changkuliers Brigade, as Lang dubbed them, proved difficult to motivate for periods longer than about twenty minutes. They would then drop their tools and squat on their haunches and smoke, until Lang roused them onto their feet again by a combination of shame, leading by example, and bribery in the form of a tin of cookies. By early afternoon, our brigade had dwindled to a handful, the remainder having retreated from the heat and dust into one of the nearby huts.

Around the Vimy, the scene was more like a carnival than a work party, with hundreds of sightseers constantly streaming past and vendors of all descriptions setting up shop next to the ropes. One persistent pedlar, equipped with a cooler on wheels, nearly drove us mad by honking his bicycle horn for hours on end. The larger operators set up temporary food stalls in the abandoned huts by the road.

It took practically both hands and both feet for me to loosen the last nut on the intake manifold at the top of the engine. As we pulled the plate away, Dan and I were astonished at the sight that greeted us: we could have been looking at a box of broken Christmas tree ornaments. There were jagged

bits of metal everywhere, and the camshaft had been broken into three pieces. One of the exhaust valves and a pushrod were missing, most likely lying in the bottom of the crankcase after having gone through a piston.

HOPE FROM ABOVE

We had been hoping all day to see the Nomad fly by, but at 3:30 p.m. we gave up and headed back up the dirt road. About half a mile up the track, we stopped to negotiate with the boss of the road workers for the use of a truck or grader to pull out the big tree stumps and smooth off the new strip. As Lang haggled, with Hona and the Major acting as interpreters, we heard in the distance the Nomad's turbine whine. Lang and I immediately scrambled onto a small motorcycle parked nearby, belonging to a policeman, and tore off back to the Vimy, zigzagging through the hundreds of sightseers coming back from the crash site. Mick was making what was probably to be his last orbit of the area when he saw us sprinting across the field to the aircraft.

Ripping off the cockpit covers, I switched on the radio. "I heard you earned the other half of your wings the other day, mate," crackled Mick's voice. "Yes, sir," I replied,

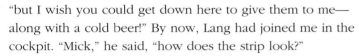

"but I wish you could get down here to give them to me—along with a cold beer!" By now, Lang had joined me in the cockpit. "Mick," he said, "how does the strip look?"

"Looks great," Mick answered, "but where is it?"

"You're just coming over it now," said Lang, as the Nomad swooshed in front of us.

"Oh—that patch there," said Mick, banking steeply. "Mate, you build a top airfield, but how about putting on another hundred yards at the north end by all those burnt stumps?"

"Will do," said Lang. "We have a grader coming tomorrow. We should be ready to take you by fifteen hundred hours."

The Nomad disappeared to the southeast, but Mick had informed us that Bob Shaw, the mechanic from the Nomad, and an interpreter were on their way to us overland and should arrive by midnight. He had also contacted Wayne Daley, our engine builder in Brisbane, who would be arriving in Jakarta in a few days with the spare engine. Psychologically, the worst was over, but we still had some hard work ahead.

DUST-OFF

The next day, Tuesday the 11th, with the able help of Bob Shaw as well as a decent set of tools, we managed to get the prop, the radiator and the gearbox off in preparation for pulling out the engine. Lang, meanwhile, put in a hard day with a creaking old power shovel, packing down the spongy surface of the airstrip and scooping out the remaining stumps. Throughout all this, the Major generously plied us with sustenance in the form of bread and butter topped Dutch-style with chocolate sprinkles.

Above, top: The local helpers balance the new engine, suspended from a log, while Corporal Bob Shaw (center) and Lang guide it into position.

Above and left: With the atmosphere already a brutal mixture of animal smells and pungent smoke, the dust from digging and then from the prop wash made it tough to breathe at all.

Above: Dan Nelson displays the remains of a piston destroyed by the exhaust valve. "You could have started a spare parts store with what I found in the oil pan," he quipped.

The Smith brothers, with Jim Bennett and Wally Shiers, hoist their repaired engine into place in Charleville, in outback Queensland. They had to forge a new connecting rod to mend their failed motor.

Above: Lumbering down the homemade strip, the Vimy winds up for takeoff. The strong crosswind is evident from the dust cloud moving to the right. The new starboard engine performed well, having test-run at full power for roughly ninety seconds before takeoff.

We grew to like our "maggot sandwiches", as they were soon labeled. Since we had no jack, Bob and I dug pits under the left wheels and slid logs under the axles to take the plane's weight while we removed the wheels and the broken parts of the undercarriage. Finally, resting the rear fuselage on a borrowed bench, we removed the tailwheel.

The light was fading when Mick swooped low overhead to move the crowd of thousands back away from the middle of the runway. He then executed a flawless landing, stirring up a cloud of dust big enough to obscure almost the entire province! Malcolm Wood, whom I had yet to meet, had to wait for about ten minutes for the air to clear before he could plunk the Islander down. As he did so, the impatient crowd of onlookers rushed forward, and it was only a matter of luck that no one was sliced by the whirling propeller blades.

We were all elated, but there was no time to celebrate. Dan grabbed the tailwheel, and he and I jumped aboard the Islander while the others piled into the Nomad. We were airborne again in a few minutes. It was a tricky takeoff, as both planes had trouble accelerating in the soft dirt. Malcolm waited until the very last moment before he yanked us into the sky. Looking down on the dusky scene below, I was mesmerized, and in a brief flash I relived the terrifying moments before the crash. Shortly after, the sight of the twinkling lights of Jakarta brought me happily back to the present.

As our grisly little band walked into the lavish Jakarta Hilton that night, covered with three days' worth of Sumatran ash and filth, the desk staff looked up in horror. But we were overjoyed at rejoining the other crews at last, and that night we celebrated our return to the 1990s in grand style. The phoenix had a flight plan to rise out of the field of ashes.

THE GREAT ESCAPE

Saturday, October 15, got off to a good start when we dropped down onto Kidby International, as the strip was now known, at 10:15 a.m. Malcolm Wood, a former British Army helicopter pilot, made the tricky task of alighting on the soft strip look positively routine. Wayne, Dan and Bob had come out the previous day to collect the deceased motor and take it back to Jakarta, so that the critical components could be stripped and fitted onto the new engine. All that then remained was to heave the new engine into place—a job that proved to require a bit too much precision for the makeshift crew of ten or twelve locals we hired for the purpose.

The idea was to raise the engine, suspended from a log, over the engine mounts and then to gently ease it into the right position. But the only instructions our helpers could understand were "up" or "down", and so they would alternately either hoist the log over their heads or practically drop the motor through the lower wing. Since the motor and the mounts had to be aligned to within one-sixteenth of an inch to thread the support bolts, this crude method was clearly hopeless. Finally, Dan and Bob slung the engine from ropes on their backs and gingerly lowered the 600-pound block into place. Seeing their legs trembling under the great weight, Mick wasted no time in driving the support bolts home.

Left and above: Liftoff Sumatra! The double-decker phoenix springs free from her six-day sentence in this remote corner of the world.

She slowly claws her way to a height of 1,000 feet above Cabang village before setting out for Jakarta, on the island of Java, 140 miles away.

By 2 p.m., we were ready to test-run the engine. Since we didn't have a timing light, Wayne had to adjust the engine by feeling the vibration. It sounded about right after three or four tries, so we decided to go for it—our engine trial having lasted all of about eight minutes.

We were now racing against daylight, as we had to be in the air by 3:30 p.m. to make it back to Jakarta before darkness fell. Everyone picked up the pace. Lang, Dan and I slid the prop out from under the left wing and dusted off a thick layer of Sumatran soil. Dan greased the hub, and the giant airscrew went on easily for once. Mick and Lang then reassembled the cowl, while Dan and I reconnected the flying wires that support the engine bay. Wayne attached the mended tailwheel strut. Our breakneck pace suited me just fine, since it kept me from thinking about the fact that we were about to levitate our kite out of this spongy dust bowl with our axles tied up with flimsy nylon ropes and an engine with less time on the clock than a two-dollar cab ride.

At 3:23 p.m., Lang started the engines—but one more problem still remained to be negotiated. Thousands of locals had gathered around us, completely covering the usable takeoff area. We waved frantically at them to clear the field, and eventually the military police stepped in and pushed the crowd back far enough to enable us to taxi to the south end of the strip. The blinding dust storm we stirred up with our prop created even more confusion, but the path ahead through the crowd was clearly narrower than our wingspan. We had no choice but to pour on the coals and hope that the spectators would dive out of our way at the crucial moment.

As we rumbled down the runway, our wheels sinking into the soft spots, we struggled to maintain control of our ship against a 10-knot crosswind. About 200 yards down the strip, I saw the front row of the crowd hit the deck just as our wings began to take effect. We had barely lifted into the air when Lang had to make a sharp left turn to clear the Nomad, which was parked at the north end of the strip. Free at last!

We circled to gain height, and on reaching 1,000 feet set out on course for Jakarta. I looked over my shoulder for what I hoped was my last glance at the scruffy patch of ground that had absorbed six of the most difficult and exhausting days of the journey—and, probably, of my entire life. The engines sounded peculiar, but they were pulling us back toward civilization, so I turned a deaf ear to them for the time being.

"We made it!" Lang shouted jubilantly, clapping me on the shoulder. "We got out!"

But I couldn't share his euphoric mood. Physically and mentally, I was worn out. I realized how fortunate we had been to survive a landing on so wild an island. But I also knew we had a long way to go yet—another 1,500 miles after Jakarta. Would the Vimy hold up? These thoughts were still filling my mind as we flew over the southern tip of Sumatra. I could see the remains of Krakatoa off our right wing. The island of Java was only a few miles ahead.

We followed the north coast and landed a couple of hours later at Halim Airport. The Nomad was with us, but the Islander had to be left behind in the field, since one of its engines failed to start. It took more than a day for the rest of the crew to make their way back to Jakarta.

Left: The volcanic landscape of central Java between Jakarta and Surabaya is beautiful but menacing. "The terrain past Sumatra didn't offer much hope if we'd had another emergency," Peter recalled. "And we were battling strong turbulence and headwinds all the way, which gave us plenty of time to think about it." The Vimy averaged just 59 miles per hour as she island-hopped 1,000 miles across Indonesia, from Java to Timor. "It was by far the toughest part of the voyage for me," said Peter.

ON THE ROAD AGAIN

We spent the next two days, Sunday the 16th and Monday the 17th, doing maintenance work and giving the left engine a thorough overhaul, to make sure it wasn't about to go the way of the right one. Our new bungee cords arrived from Germany on Tuesday, and once we had wrapped them around the axles, we were ready to give the new engine a proper test flight. We flew to the Smith brothers' original landing site at Kalijati, a distance of 60 miles, but on our return, I noticed that the exhaust gas temperature

was unusually high. I had also had trouble synchronizing the propellers during the flight. Maybe I was just being oversensitive, I told myself. But there was some good news as well. Malcolm Wood had managed to limp home in the Islander that afternoon, although he would have to remain in Jakarta for several more days awaiting a new fuel-control unit.

The following morning, the 19th, we set off for Surabaya. It was a miserable flight, fighting extreme turbulence and headwinds all the way, and it took us more than six and a half hours to travel only 378 miles.

 Latitude 6°31'S, longitude 107°39'E

"Where did Jim go?" Lang (right) says to Peter. The pilot's white knuckles clearly show that flying the ancient beast is a two-handed task. The cramped confines of the Vimy's cockpit are evident, as is the importance of the elbow guards on each side, which prevent the pilots' arms from being shortened accidently. Barely visible at the bottom are the feet of photographer Jim Stanfield, who is standing up behind the pilots looking down on Kalijati, in Indonesia.

Above and right: The Vimy flies over the grass airfield at Kalijati, in Indonesia. This field was the first built in what was then the Dutch East Indies, and housed a primitive flying school when Ross Smith and crew landed here on December 6, 1919. The Japanese occupied the base during World War II, and several of their hangars remain. An Indonesian DC-3, visible at upper left, escorted the modern Vimy to Kalijati. The 60-mile trip from Jakarta was a good shakedown flight for the Vimy after the crew, now joined by Wayne Daley, had spent three days at Jakarta's Halim Airport repairing the landing gear and tuning the engines.

Wayne Daley had substantially detuned the engines to make them run cooler, but this inevitably took its toll on our performance.

As we made our way along the north coast of Java, we passed a few World War II-vintage shipwrecks and saw several volcanoes rising to a height of more than 10,000 feet off to the south. I was thankful for any distraction that kept me from thinking about the sure destruction that awaited us if we were forced down again over this last 1,500-mile stretch. We had had one miraculous escape. There would be no such luck a second time. As we circled over the city of Surabaya, I scanned the area below, wondering where exactly it was that the Smith brothers had built their bamboo runway seventy-five years ago.

We set out for Bali on the morning of Thursday the 20th, and were once again plagued by headwinds in excess of 25 knots. We had difficulty climbing over even the lower ridges extending between two volcanoes on the eastern

ROOFS TO THE RESCUE

My brother and I had decided that it would be impossible to get the Vimy into the air in the usual way, so we consulted with our invaluable friend, the [Harbor Board] engineer, and he agreed to collect bamboo matting from far and wide, so that we might construct a mat-paved roadway.

I observed that this matting formed the principal covering of the native huts, and subsequently learned that entire villages in the immediate vicinity were stripped bare to provide us with the necessary materials....

Next morning saw us at the aërodrome by daylight, and a gladsome sight met our eyes. Natives were streaming in from every direction bearing sheets of bamboo matting—they were literally carrying their houses on their backs—and already a great pile of it lay by the Vimy.

...just twenty-four hours after our arrival at Soerabaya, [we] made a sensational take-off, with the mats flying in all directions.

ROSS SMITH IN SURABAYA, INDONESIA,
DECEMBER 7–8, 1919

Ross Smith took this photograph in Surabaya on December 8, 1919, as villagers laid bamboo matting pulled from their own huts to rescue the Vimy from what he described as *a pond of semi-liquid mud.*

Above: Virtually all of the flat lands and many volcanic hillsides of Java are cultivated, to feed the world's fifth most-populated nation. The rice paddies are brown and barren at the end of the dry season, but will be transformed into so many square ponds by the imminent monsoon rains.

Right: The eastern tip of Java falls behind as the Vimy crosses the Straits of Bali. Peter's confidence was waning. "After the long hours we had spent crossing the volcanoes, jungles and paddy fields of Java, I couldn't wait to get out over water again," he said. "But it only took a few minutes over the sea to realize that maybe things weren't much better out there. At least Bali offered a few broad beaches we could land on."

extremity of Java, and at one point I had to circle several times, using the lift from updrafts along the ridge to gain sufficient height. Knowing what little chance of survival we had if the Vimy let us down over these unbroken stretches of spinach-green jungle, we were greatly relieved when we came upon the Straits of Bali. We made a gradual gliding descent through puffy clouds down to 1,000 feet, and then followed the beaches to Denpasar. It had taken us more than three hours to travel just 170 miles.

At Denpasar, we took on a full fuel load, knowing there would be no avgas between here and Timor, but again our performance was penalized. It was touch and go whether we made it over the palm trees at the end of the 8,000-foot runway. Over the next twenty

minutes, we clawed our way to 1,500 feet, but the Vimy could climb no further. Hopping over the island of Flores, we then crossed about 60 miles of water to reach the large, irregularly shaped island of Sumbawa. Looking down, we saw it to be covered almost from end to end with hundreds and hundreds of rice paddies divided by the same kind of earth ridges that had done such damage to our undercarriage.

It was late in the day when we saw the airfield at Bima. This was one of the fields the colonial Dutch government built especially for the 1919 race, and at close quarters, it didn't seem to have changed much since those days. We rented huts at the edge of a beautiful bay, but found the power to be out. The manager offered Dan a free meal to fix his defunct

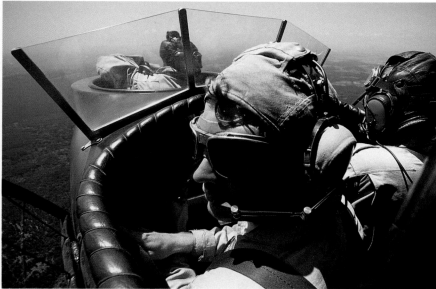

Above: Peter keeps an eye on the left engine gauges, while Lang checks the map and Dan enjoys the unobstructed view from the crow's nest. The date is October 20, and the plane is en route from Surabaya to Bali's Denpasar Airport for a refueling stop before proceeding to Bima.

generator, but this was a hopeless task in the total darkness. Darkness was no bar to a swim, however, and we jumped into the little hotel pool, some of us still wearing our flight suits (poor man's laundry). Our good spirits rose even further as we looked across a shimmering lagoon to see a full moon rising majestically from behind a volcano.

The following day's flight to Kupang, a village on the island of Timor, was a little more upbeat, since the headwinds had abated and the engines were singing a slightly happier song than they had for the last few days. It was October 21 when we passed over Kimodo Island, home of the famous man-eating lizards. Not surprisingly, it looked to be very sparsely populated. Another hour or so down the track, circling over a volcano, we got a commanding view down into the crater, with its pool of bubbling green water, along with a noseful of the pungent smell of sulfur. We then turned southward toward Timor for our longest water crossing since Crete: a distance of 174 miles.

The only ground-to-air photograph in Sir Ross Smith's account of his flight in *National Geographic* shows the Vimy flying across the lush terrain of Java. Here is how he described it: *[W]e sped rapidly over fertile tracts of this amazing island…Java impressed me as one vast bounteous garden, amid which rise the immense, shapely cones of volcanic mountains.*

Below and right: Flying over the Indonesian island of Sumbawa reveals thousands of fish farms, which provide a welcome staple food but not much choice for a pilot faced with a forced landing. Ross Smith made the same observation: *From the point of view of a prospective forced landing, the 400-mile flight to Bima was impossible. Not a single flat occurred on which we might have landed. Scenically, this lap was glorious.*

Above: Some of the inhabitants of Bima, on the Indonesian island of Sumbawa. The crew enjoyed fresh fish in the village, as did their predecessors in 1919. Unlike seventy-five years ago, there was no local sultan on hand to greet them, but the modern flyers were warmly welcomed by a small group of local officials and billeted in comfortable huts on the bay. Lang in particular enjoyed the simple solitude. "Bima was the best place we stayed in on the whole trip," he said.

Left and above: Latitude 8°54'S, longitude 121°39'E The Vimy approaches a steaming volcano on the island of Flores. Not far from here, in 1815, Tambora erupted, ejecting 44 cubic miles of pumice and ash into the atmosphere and turning 1816 into an endless winter for Europe and North America. "The smell of sulfur was overwhelming," recalled Jim Stanfield, who had been appropriately berthed in the nose cockpit. "But at least the volcano wasn't too angry."

Ross Smith skirted the coast of Bali, but, flying over Java, was enchanted by the sight of *a thousand isles...one of the most beautiful sights I have ever looked down upon*. This contemporary photograph shows sacred idols in temple grounds in Bali.

Left: Young boys frolic with their ponies in the surf on the Indonesian island of Timor. The peaceful scene at sunset belies anxiety about the final flight the next day. "Lang seemed fine," Peter said, "but I was a wreck at the thought that the plane and our whole project might yet disappear into the sea on the last lap."

Above: The pilots are greeted on Timor with traditional dances, flowers and handloomed scarves.

Tomorrow would be the great day whereupon reposed the destiny of our hopes, labors, and ideals.

ROSS SMITH ON TIMOR, THE NIGHT BEFORE DEPARTING FOR DARWIN, DECEMBER 9, 1919

But I knew the risks ahead of us on this long stretch were minimal compared to those Ross Smith and his crew had faced. We at least could call for help, whereas they would have had no hope of rescue had they ditched into these remote waters.

As we approached Kupang, the control tower asked us to orbit the town for the benefit of the local school children. On landing, we were welcomed by dancing girls in ceremonial dress, musicians playing traditional instruments, and chanting old men, their teeth heavily stained from years of chewing betel nut.

At sunset, I took a walk on the beach with Chris Weber. As we watched young boys galloping their ponies in the surf, I thought about the little boat that came ashore near here in 1789 with Captain Bligh and his band of eighteen loyal crewmen, more than 3,000 miles from where they had been cast adrift by the mutineers on HMS *Bounty*—one of the greatest feats of seamanship and navigation ever. "Our jaunt tomorrow is paltry by comparison," I said cheerily to Chris. "Only eight hours over five hundred miles." But I think she knew I was dreading every minute of it.

Above: Dan tightens the flying wires and applies tape to keep them from chafing. "We gave her a good lookover that morning," he remembered, "but then we had to wave goodbye and cross our fingers. It was tough watching from the ground as they set off, but they needed the extra fuel more than they needed me."

Peter samples the fuel, checking for water in the tanks. The preflight ritual was carried out with a bit more reverence than usual this morning, October 22. Not satisfied with technical checks, certain crew members resorted to superstition.

No Prize for Failure

After a restless night, during which my anxious mind went over every moving part of the aircraft, we made our way to El Tari Airport on the morning of Saturday October 22, our forty-second day since leaving England. The Vimy made a striking sight as she stood silhouetted against the red rising sun, her flying wires glinting in the early morning light like so many crossed sabers. Such a solid and worthy machine, I thought, so why so many fears and doubts? And as for me, known as the group cheerleader, the eternal optimist, have I just been fooling myself and everybody else all along? My anxiety had reached a crescendo, but deep down I knew why.

This final flight to Darwin was different. It would end with total success or total failure. Failure would mean the disappearance of the Vimy, and with her would go the efforts of so many people over the past two years. There wouldn't even be any wreckage to mourn over. Within minutes of any engine failure, the waves of the Timor Sea would be hungrily lapping at the letters G-EAOU as our upper wing slipped forever beneath the surface.

I tried to buck myself up with a false sense of optimism. "We are destined to succeed," I told myself. "Fortune shines upon us." But fortune is fickle, as I knew, and while success may seem deserved by hard work, it must finally be bestowed by Fate. Resorting to superstition, I began looking for a four-leaf clover (or any kind of clover!) in the long grass that had sprung up around a Japanese pillbox a few yards from where the Vimy was tied down.

Walking across to join the other members of the crew, I found them already discussing our arrival time. This struck me as a little presumptuous. I heard the engines bark to life as Dan did a quick warm-up to check the new spark plugs. "You ready, boss?" he shouted down to me above the rumble of the idling motors. I nodded without much conviction.

I put on my Mae West and strapped myself in, feeling in awe of the moment. Lang didn't much care for any ceremony. He just wanted

212

to get in and go home. The radio crackled to life: "Vimy One cleared to Darwin. Advise when ready for takeoff." There was a long pause, and then came: "Good luck, gentlemen."

Even with only the two of us on board, our initial rate of climb was startlingly slow, owing to our full fuel load of two and a quarter tons. The propellers were hard to synchronize, and this set up an unpleasant pulse throughout the aircraft. A few hills lay between us and the sea, and we only just managed to scrape over them at our height of 1,200 feet. The best we could manage was 1,400 feet, and it took us more than twenty minutes to reach that.

To me, the engines sounded adequate but not brilliant. Although he didn't say anything, Lang seemed to agree, since he kept us hugging the coast as long as possible. But eventually we had to let go. We turned to the right, tracking southeast direct to Darwin. Bearing: 121 degrees; distance: 441 nautical miles; time to destination: 7 hours and 16 minutes—so said our brilliant little navigation box. Just over seven hours to victory!

Soon the green and brown visible over my left shoulder disappeared, and there was only blue. After a few hours, our groundspeed was still poor, around 66 knots, which meant we had a headwind of at least 10 knots at our altitude of 2,000 feet. "We might pick up a few knots if we go lower," I said to Lang. "Yes," he replied, "but we might need the extra time to squeal

All or nothing. The Vimy slugs her way forward, laden with fuel for the eight-hour flight across the Timor Sea to Australia. Fortunately, the runway here at Kupang, on the island of Timor, is more than a mile and a half long. "We barely managed to scrape over the hills," said Peter, "since she quit climbing at fourteen hundred feet."

Keith Smith's photograph of, left to right, Wally Shiers, Jim Bennett and Ross Smith drinking to success before their flight to Australia. Bad local water made coconut milk more a necessity than a novelty.

Success in reach! The emerging coastline of Australia is a gladsome sight for Lang and Peter after they have been looking at nothing but the blue waters of the Timor Sea for six hours. "We saw only half a dozen boats over more than four hundred miles of water," Lang told reporters in Darwin. "Even though it was my country, Peter was the first to send up a cheer." "Lang had to concentrate on keeping the plane level, the horizon was so hazy," added Peter. "I was free to look around, since there wasn't much map reading to do."

for help." Each thousand feet of height would give us another six or seven minutes in the air in the event of an engine failure.

We droned along, traveling at just over a mile a minute. The least bit of turbulence changed the note of the engines, sending my pulse racing for a few seconds. I would stare at the tachometer to detect any variation and then scold myself for my lack of confidence. "Resign yourself to your fate and quit worrying—and quit staring at the instruments!" But after a few minutes, I would peek again: fuel pressure, oil pressure, water temp, exhaust temp, RPMs—the same sequence a thousand times over, as my emotions

lurched through their own obsessive cycle of fear, resolution, confidence, fear.

The fear that seized my heart was not fear of any mortal danger but an immense fear of failure. Already I could hear the voices of doom passing judgment: "What a pity, so close." "Good effort. Too bad about the Vimy." "Those fools should have quit in Sumatra."

The sky was still veiled in morning haze, but at about the halfway mark, a few puffy clouds appeared, making it easier to keep the plane oriented. Catching sight of a few sailboats on our right side, I marked their position on the map: 10°55'S, 126°01'E. They would make a good ditching target in an

MID-TIMOR MEETING

CROSSING THE SHARK-INFESTED Timor Sea was the part of the flight the competitors were most anxious about. Ditching into these waters meant almost certain death. The Vimy's crew were as much at risk as any of the other teams should one of their engines fail, for in those days, twin-engine planes were unable to maintain height on one engine. Having two motors in fact doubled the chances of engine failure.

Seeking to reduce the risk, the Australian government ordered the cruiser HMAS *Sydney* to patrol the middle section of the 466-mile route over water. The warship would not only act as a navigation aid but might also be able to steam to the assistance of any downed flyers.

Three hours after leaving Timor, the Vimy's crew sighted the plume of smoke on the horizon marking the *Sydney*'s position. Half an hour later, they were overhead the four-funnel cruiser. Ross Smith had fond memories of the *Sydney* protecting the convoy in which he had sailed from Australia to Egypt in 1914. During that voyage, the *Sydney* had been diverted to intercept and sink the German cruiser *Emden*. He wrote: *[W]e knew now that, whatever might*

befall, we had a friend at hand. We swooped low, and exactly at twelve minutes past noon passed over the vessel, seeing plainly the upturned faces of the sailors and their waving hands.

Above: As the Vimy circled overhead, a sailor took this photograph from the deck of HMAS *Sydney*, seen below in a bird's-eye view taken by Ross Smith.

Knowing the warship's exact position, the airmen were able to work out their groundspeed (75 miles per hour). Years later, in a radio interview, Shiers recalled the morale-boosting midsea meeting with the *Sydney*: *We flew around it and we gave the boys [sailors] a good outing [time] and a good eye [look] at our old machine.*

As they circled the warship, Ross Smith dropped a bottle attached to a small parachute into the sea below. It included the message "All's well!" Sailors retrieved the bottle, and the *Sydney* radioed Darwin that the Vimy was only 180 miles away. The news raced through the tiny frontier port, and everyone rushed to Fannie Bay airfield to greet the first plane ever to land at Darwin.

Above: *Sydney* crewmen watch the circling Vimy.

Left: The message bottle dropped from the Vimy. At right is the crew's message, which continues: *Very glad to see you. Many thanks for looking after us. Going strong.* On the left is a sighting report written by the *Sydney*'s captain.

emergency. The GPS was showing 220 miles, or three hours and eighteen minutes, to go. Our groundspeed had picked up to 68 knots; the engines sounded more consistent. The voices of doom grew faint, and I no longer needed to puff up as much courage to drown them out.

At 135 miles, we had two hours left to run. Lang and I began to talk a bit more, even venturing to consider our arrival procedure. At 95 miles, I could faintly pick up the controllers from Darwin and began to fantasize about how the city would look on our approach. I had a clear image in my mind of the Vimy's shadow passing over the memorial to the Smith brothers that stands near the coast.

Haze plays tricks with your distance vision, but I thought I saw a thin white line to our left. Above it, a flash of pale green

was emerging. "Over there," I said to Lang. "That's Bathurst Island, right?" "Yep," he replied. "Welcome to Australia."

We still had 22 miles to go when I saw the city of Darwin. A gaggle of planes and helicopters was standing by ready to greet us, and this was causing some confusion for the air traffic controllers. As we came closer, I could make out the headland of Fannie Bay, where the original Vimy touched down on December 10, 1919. We crossed the coastline, and I almost exploded with excitement. Success was ours!

We circled the city and banked left toward the airport. As our nose dipped below the horizon, the rich red earth of the Northern Territory was revealed. Lang pulled the throttles, and I could hear the song of the wind rushing through our flying wires. I took a deep breath, savoring every sense of the

LAND HO!
An hour later both of us saw ahead and to port what appeared to be haze, but which we hoped was land, though neither dared express his hopes. They were justified, however, ten minutes later, and hailing Bennett and Shiers, we pointed joyfully to Bathurst Island lighthouse.

ROSS SMITH OVER
BATHURST ISLAND,
DECEMBER 10, 1919

Left, top: Latitude 12°25'S, longitude 130°52'E
The sign says it all. The Vimy is frozen just a split second before touching Terra Australis, as Ross Smith referred to his home soil when he touched down on December 10, 1919—his first homecoming in more than four years. "Landing in Darwin was the culmination of all our dreams and efforts," said Peter. Indeed, the modern Vimy crew had endured much: foul weather, fatigue and, occasionally, despair, but what better demonstration that the true pioneering spirit still lives.

Left: Cheers and hugs of joy start even as the Vimy taxis to a halt on the runway at Darwin. Peter (left) and Lang still have their life jackets on after the eight-hour water crossing. Dan (center) jumped on board to kiss the plane he helped build for passing her toughest test.

217

Above: Time for bubbles. Lang takes a more modest portion than Peter (holding the bottle). The champagne was sent by Pol Roger, the French vintner who brought a magnum to greet the crew on their first landing at Troyes, in France.

Above, center: In their pith helmets, or "solar topees" (faithful replicas of those worn by the original Vimy's crew), the pilots answer questions from reporters in Darwin. "We hope people will now have a better understanding of how the pioneers of the air contributed to the modern world," said the Australian flyer. "Someone had to take the risk of being first."

moment. Then the announcement came over the control tower: "Vimy One cleared to land. Welcome back to Darwin after all these years."

The Vimy's wheels touched down on Australian soil at 3:09 p.m. on October 22, 1994. We bounced once, to the delight of the dozens of photographers lining the runway. As we slowed down, Dan and Jim arrived alongside in a jeep and jumped onto the lower wing to ride up to the waiting crowd. The official welcoming committee came forward to greet us, and we were delighted to see among the many dignitaries the faces of some old friends, including Jenny Moseley and Peter Miller from National Geographic and, of course, Kevin Weldon of Weldon Owen.

Lang and I stood in the cockpit for a moment, and several photographers asked us to hold the pose, but after seven and a half hours of relentless anxiety we wanted to walk on Australian soil. Lang was greeted by his wife, Bev, and his two daughters, Kylie and Katrina. Someone handed me a magnum of Pol Roger champagne, and I let the cork fly. It arced triumphantly into the air and bounced off the upper wing, to the cheers of the crowd.

The administrator of the Northern Territory, Dr. Austin Asche, and the Acting Lord Mayor

of Darwin, Robyne Burridge, stepped forward to shake our hands, just as their counterparts had greeted Ross Smith. Then a woman handed me a telegram from the Australian Prime Minister, Paul Keating, congratulating us on our "adventurous and pioneering spirit". I felt doubly honored when she told me she was Wendy Miles, the daughter of Sir Hudson Fysh, one of the founders of Qantas and the first person to shake Ross Smith's hand on that great day seventy-five years ago, surprising him with a bundle of telegrams from around the world, including one from Prime Minister Billy Hughes. The two young men had served in the Middle East campaigns of World War I, and Fysh had traveled overland from Longreach to Darwin in a Model T Ford to witness his old friend's moment of triumph. Wendy Miles looked up at our giant machine and said, "I remember seeing Ross Smith's Vimy on display when I was a little girl. Seeing the plane again today gave me a funny feeling inside. I was quite overcome."

The rest of the day remains a blur in my mind. There were lots of pictures and speeches and celebrations, but what I will always remember is a feeling of relief and

pride rather than jubilation. Through the efforts of so many people, we had produced a wonderful time machine and had surveyed the world at the leisurely speed of 75 miles per hour.

The storms in Europe, the plague in India and our forced landing in Sumatra had all taken their toll, adding two weeks to the flight time the Smith brothers had recorded back in 1919. But I was still well pleased with our achievement. It had been very much a team effort, and Lang's fortitude in particular had made the difference.

The Smiths had unquestionably endured far more personal risks, but they had climbed into a state-of-the-art factory airplane with few strings attached. We, on the other hand, had built our own Vimy from the ground up—and substantially with borrowed money, all of which I was accountable for. While I had come to the conclusion that I was, alas, not a truly fearless soul like Captain Ross Smith, I was not ashamed either, because I knew that the pressures I had faced were probably more complex.

As we pushed our travel-worn but sturdy machine into the hangar that evening, I could faintly make out names and greetings in Arabic, Hindi, Malay and other languages traced in the dusty surface of the lower wings. It was my privilege to understand what Ross Smith had written about this moment:

The hardships and perils of the past month were forgotten in the excitement of the present. We shook hands with one another, our hearts swelling with those emotions invoked by achievement and the glamour of the moment. It was, and will be, perhaps, the supreme hour of our lives.

Top: "We had a great adventure," said Peter. "I think the mishaps made our flight a real living biography of the Smith brothers. Except they made it two weeks faster than we did. So much for progress in the last seventy-five years." The crew were greeted by the modern counterparts and relatives of those who witnessed the landing of the first Vimy.

Above: The pilots stand on the spot where the original Vimy first touched down on Australian soil. The field at Darwin's Fannie Bay had been specially constructed for the occasion. The original landing ground, adjacent to the modern airport, is now a housing development, but the main road is named Ross Smith Avenue.

Epilogue:
Touching the Past

EPILOGUE: TOUCHING THE PAST

Above: In a bank to the left, the biplane enjoys the still air of early morning over central Australia. The whistle-stop tour took almost a month, and saw 6,000 miles of the island continent.

FROM DARWIN, it was as far to our final destination of Adelaide as it would have been to fly back to Calcutta. But it certainly didn't feel that way. Every leg of this flight would be over firm, dry and friendly ground. And this time, we would be largely on our own. We said fond goodbyes in Darwin to the television crew, Chris Weber, Bob Poole, and Mark Roy. Joe Stancampiano and Jenny Moseley, from Geographic, and Sean Maffett, from the BBC, would leave us there as well.

Right: Even the huge biplane is swallowed up in the vastness of Australia. Although the flights across the outback were long, and often bumpy and cold, the terrain was flat and friendly. The pilots found the "inland sea" greatly preferable to the Timor Sea.

Previous page: Latitude 33°51'S, longitude 151°13'E
The Vimy glides southward toward the metropolis of Sydney. After touring above Sydney Harbour, the reincarnation of G-EAOU opened the new runway at Sydney (Kingsford Smith) Airport—known as Mascot Aerodrome when Ross Smith landed there seventy-five years earlier.

Below: Latitude 34°56'S, longitude 138°31'E
The original Vimy G-EAOU rests proudly in Adelaide, where she landed triumphantly in March 1920. This was Ross Smith's first homecoming in five years. The modern crew made a pilgrimage here, to touch the "old bus". Her interior woodwork still bears signatures and greetings written by the crew and the factory workers at Brooklands.

Right: Eastern Queensland offered bright-green rolling hills and farmlands. "We would get airborne at sunrise each morning, fly for a few hours, and land at a farm or roadhouse for breakfast," Peter recalled. "Country warmth and baked beans and eggs were available at every stop." His Australian seatmate, Lang, was heading for home. "With every passing hour, the terrain became more familiar," he said.

THE WINNING TEAM

But the hardest breakup came when we said goodbye to our support plane crews. Malcolm Wood had done such brave flying in the Islander after Ian Snell went down with what turned out to be cholera and blackwater fever. Corporal Bob Shaw, the Nomad's engineer, had helped us all along the way and had forged a lifelong friendship with his fellow mechanic Dan Nelson. Gary Tierney had proved himself a worthy copilot and had, in fact, done much of the camera flying in the Nomad. But perhaps the real hero of the group was Major Mick Reynolds, who had overcome tremendous obstacles just to secure the Nomad for our use and had given us outstanding logistical and safety support, enabling us to procure the best possible photographic record of our epic journey.

We left Darwin after two days of celebration, and were joined by Erik Durfey, who designed the Vimy's electrical system, flying a rented Cessna. Mark Rebholz and his wife, Patty, flying an old Bellanca, met up with us at most of our stops. No longer were we encumbered by diplomatic clearances, flight planning, or the logistics of search and survival procedures. Several of the legs would be long and quite cold, as we had to fly as high as 8,000 feet to avoid the turbulence rising off the warm red center of Australia, but my spirits were riding high on pride in our achievement.

Above: Especially in Australia, the Vimy drew crowds of all ages. Many schoolchildren did projects on the Vimy flights past and present. "We must have lifted ten thousand kids up to have a look in the cockpit," said a weary Mark Rebholz. "All but a few asked, 'Where do you go to the bathroom?'" Even the rugged stockmen in tiny outback towns who came by to have a look at her showed a childlike fascination with the vintage airplane.

We made overnight stops at many little outback towns, including Tennant Creek, Cloncurry, Longreach and Charleville. Departing at sunrise, we would fly for a few glorious hours in the cool morning air and then drop in on a cattle station or roadhouse for breakfast. In the vast expanses of the Northern Territory and Queensland, virtually every settlement has an airstrip.

Most of the towns we visited were ports of call on Ross Smith's tour of Australia in 1919, and a surprising number of the people who came to greet us brought along pictures and memories of the great Australian heroes and the giant bird that delivered them safely from England. We were similarly fêted, and had only to circle a town a few times to see a stream of cars rapidly converging on the airport from all directions to watch us land. The crowds would press up against the airplane, and almost before the propellers had stopped, we would be caught up in a frenzy of signing everything from hats and shirts to all manner of outstretched pieces of paper.

Lang and I would tell stories for the schoolkids, while Dan, Mark and Erik helped the eager onlookers, young and old alike, up onto the wing to have a look inside the cockpit. Throughout the trip, it never ceased to amaze us how the Vimy struck a tactile nerve in everyone who saw her.

AN ACT OF PROVIDENCE

Charleville, lying deep inland in Queensland, had particular significance for us. The Smith brothers, along with Wally Shiers and Jim Bennett, had been stranded there for more than fifty days before they made their way on to Sydney and points south. Their left engine failed, forcing them down in a scrubby field known as Ward Plain, about 10 miles outside Charleville. The head of the local historical society, George Balsillie, invited us to come out and see the original landing site, where the Vimy had been tied under a tree during her lengthy stay while Ross, Keith and Jim Bennett went to the Ipswich Railway Works to oversee the construction of a new propeller and connecting rod. Wally stayed behind to keep an eye on the plane.

We were taken to see a weathered and dented historical marker standing at the edge of Ward Plain. "The marker is only here

because of the road," George told us, pointing toward an old grove of trees in the bush. "I think the Vimy was actually tied down about four hundred yards over that way." As we looked across to the trees, he added, "The land has never been any good for farming, and I've heard it said there are some old fuel cans still out there." Lang, Dan, Jim, Erik and I immediately raced off into the weeds on a treasure hunt for the rusty tin cans, on the chance that they had been overlooked as junk for the past seventy-five years.

We had been poking around for perhaps twenty minutes when Lang found part of a fuel can with the Shell emblem stamped into the top. Deeper in the underbrush, Dan came upon a 4-gallon tin, rusty but intact. One corner bore the words "Shell Benzine—Made in Sumatra", and on the opposite side was stamped "Shell Spirit—Imperial Oil Co. Ltd." These marks left us in no doubt that the cans had been left behind by the original Vimy crew. I'm sure the locals thought we were mad as we ran around the field like kids around a Christmas tree. But no one else could have felt as we did about the rusty old cans discarded by those four courageous men three-quarters of a century ago. It was as if the original crew had led us here to the end of our rainbow.

✴ *Left and below*: Latitude 25°22'S, longitude 146°14'E After lying for seventy-five years in a vacant field near Charleville, in Queensland, fuel cans left behind by the original Vimy team were found by the modern-day crew. The remote location and the unusual imprint on the cans, "Shell Benzine", put their authenticity beyond doubt. Although battered and rusty, the containers were as precious as the Holy Grail to the modern flyers, who had been through so much to pay homage to their predecessors.

Opposite page: Tracking down the east coast of Australia, the crew enjoyed a view of the pristine beaches and the deep blue of the Pacific Ocean just south of Coffs Harbour.

Above: After landing the first aircraft on the new runway at Sydney Airport on November 4, 1994, Peter and Lang were greeted by Prime Minister Paul Keating. Speeches ran overtime, forcing the Vimy to orbit overhead for forty minutes until the freshly laid asphalt was clear.

As I knelt down in the tall grass of Ward Plain, in the long afternoon shadow of a eucalyptus tree, I had a warm feeling, a sense of completion. I had started out in search of this forgotten hero two years ago, and the quest had meant giving up my job, my house, my savings, everything in my life that represented security. And I had suffered a few moments of mortal fear as well. Like a thunderbolt, it hit me that had I not endured all these hardships, I would never have found Ross Smith. It was in our determination more than in our skill or luck or courage that our efforts mirrored his. As long as we never gave up, his spirit was there to guide us. My fears had been unwarranted. We had been destined to succeed.

THE SKIES REMEMBER

We continued our tour of Australia along the east coast, greeted everywhere by swelling crowds of well-wishers. Lang was mobbed by friends and family in his home town of Brisbane. In Sydney, we were given the honor of being the first aircraft to land on the new runway at Sydney (Kingsford Smith) Airport. We ended up having to circle around the airport and Botany Bay quite a few times, as the official speeches by the politicians below ran well overtime. Eventually, the "hot air" show was adjourned, and the waiting crowd cleared sufficiently for us to land. It was not my best effort, and the scrawl of black tire marks I left on the runway will remain as my autograph until the next repaving. The Prime Minister, Paul Keating, greeted us cordially and was kind enough not to comment on my landing technique.

G-EAOU is refueled in February 1920. A few of the cans seen here were left behind in this field, to be found by the modern Vimy crew.

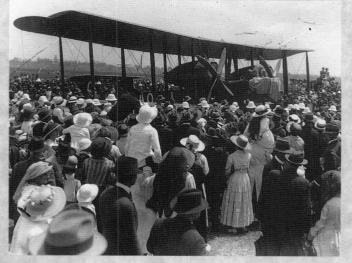

A great crowd gathered to meet the Vimy when she landed at Sydney's Mascot Aerodrome on February 14, 1920.

Our flying circus went on to Adelaide, but severe winds, cold weather and minor technical problems forced the Vimy down six times during this last thousand miles. We spent four days in Adelaide, the home of Ross and Keith Smith and the final resting place of the original Vimy G-EAOU.

Sadly, the old bus has been poorly restored and looks as though she was repainted with a mop. But her spirit still whispers to those who listen, as does the spirit of her crew and of the men and women who built her back in England. Inside one of the little wooden access doors, I found signatures and wishes of "bon voyage" dated October 1919 written by the workers at Brooklands. I couldn't help but think of the bittersweet ending to the Smith brothers' story.

Ross and Keith Smith returned to England in 1921 to be knighted by King George V. Jim Bennett joined them, his thirst for adventure persuading him to sell the auto repair shop he had started with his share of the prize money. Only Wally Shiers opted for the safety of domestic life and remained in his native Australia. It was a case of *déjà vu* as the crew found themselves back at Brooklands early in 1922, preparing for the first flight around the world at the same frenzied pace as they had prepared for their pioneering flight to Australia.

WHOM THE GODS LOVE, DIES YOUNG

The Vickers company had proposed that the Australian heroes attempt the round-the-world flight in a Viking amphibious aircraft. The Viking was a three-year-old design, but it was tricky to fly and had not been mass-produced. On the morning of Thursday April 13, 1922, a huge crowd had gathered at Brooklands to see Captain Sir Ross Smith take the Viking's controls. Stanley Cockerell, Vickers' chief test pilot, gave a quick demonstration flight in the weird-looking machine, which seemed to have more in common with a motorboat than an aircraft. Everything was ready except Keith. The more deliberate and cautious older brother, traveling down from London by train, was delayed by fog. Despite his impetuous and fearless nature, Ross insisted on waiting for him, perhaps out of superstition, but more likely because he wanted to share the accolades.

Eventually, the press prevailed upon Ross to go ahead, pleading that they had to speed their pictures back to London in time for the afternoon papers. "C'mon, Benny, let's give it a go," Ross said to Jim Bennett, who agreed, but with some hesitation. Within minutes of their takeoff, Keith arrived to see the Viking spinning earthward and smashing into the banking at the far end of the track. He was

Above: Minutes before their tragic death on April 13, 1922, Sir Ross Smith and Jim Bennett pose in front of the Vickers Viking amphibian with designer Rex Pierson (center). Keith Smith was to have been the third member of the crew, and was saved only by a train delay.

among the first to reach the crumpled wreck. Ross was killed on impact, and Jim Bennett died moments later in Keith's arms.

Ross Smith was dead. Like Icarus, the Greek hero of myth, he was fearless but not invincible. But his legacy is great. He left an indelible imprint on our modern-day world, where thousands of travelers are whisked across time zones and continents every day. Ross Smith paid the ultimate price. Like all explorers, he knew that seeking new frontiers can be a dangerous and costly endeavor. But risk has never dissuaded those fired with a burning desire to know what's out there. It is the very lifeblood of human achievement.

I hope that our flight revived that spirit of adventure and discovery. Even in our safe, modern world, where people spend so much energy seeking protection and indemnity from life's dangers, there are still pioneers—those who dare to be first in any field. And it is these brave men and women who bridge the gap between fanciful ideas and real progress. I think that those who saw our magnificent machine, if only for a moment, felt a renewed sense of adventure, along with the spirit of optimism that is essential for any idea to get off the ground.

Above all, I had realized my dream. I had seen the world as no one else had for seventy-five years. I had been carried by the spirits of the past through the numerous challenges of the present. The Vimy had truly become a time machine.

Dan Nelson and I shed a few tears as the big gray doors of the hangar clanged shut. The Vimy was peacefully put to bed at Luskintyre Airfield, north of Sydney, Australia, where she will remain in storage until—who knows? Well, wherever she is, her nose will always point to adventure.

Above, left: The sun sets on the Vimy expedition. In retracing the "greatest flight", she has cast her shadow over half the world. She finished slightly bruised and dusty, her wings and wires splotched with oil, but she had achieved both of her goals. The Vimy reminded millions of the courage it took to be first. And she transported her modern crew back into the past to experience the adventure of a lifetime.

HE WAS JUST A YOUNG MAN

Ross Smith and party arrived here from Charleville at 3:30 p.m. yesterday—he stayed the night at Fitzgerald Hotel and left this morning for Narromine, [a] shade over 200 miles [by air].

I was introduced to the party last night, Ross Smith is in build rather tall and of typical cornstalk build—complexion rusty, freckled, blue-grey eyes—aquiline real hard case features you could chop wood with—age 25 and a manner truly casual Australian...

I was lucky to be here and meet Smith and have a real good look all over the machine—I got a snapshot taken an hour before they left Bourke which I enclose as it will give you a much better idea.

Dad.

FROM A LETTER WRITTEN TO HIS SON BY WILLIAM ADAMS OF SYDNEY DURING A VISIT TO BOURKE, NEW SOUTH WALES, FEBRUARY 13, 1920

FROM DREAMS TO WINGS

"Where do we go from here?"

EARLY IN 1993, Lang Kidby and I had made the decision to seriously examine the practicability of building a replica of the Vickers Vimy—the biplane that can truly be said to have conquered the world. I suspected that a set of plans existed somewhere, because I knew that a replica had been built in 1969 but had been destroyed in a fire, probably sparked by a static charge, while parked on the ground in Manchester, England, only weeks after making its first flight. We found copies of the original 1918 plans used to build that replica after a frantic worldwide search. Eventually, we made contact with all the main players associated with the 1969 project, and their support was to become invaluable.

To make the aircraft aerodynamically original, we had to retain the enormous four-bladed propellers, which turn at a maximum speed of 1,050 RPM. The Rolls Royce Eagle engines used in Ross Smith's plane haven't been produced for seventy years and turned at half the RPM of modern engines of similar power. We therefore had to find a powerplant that could produce at least 350 horsepower and, since today's engines turn so much faster than those built early this century, could be combined with a gearbox to reduce the engine revolutions to one-fourth of the engine speed. A Chevrolet V-8 was chosen because of its availability and reliability. The gearbox, we soon found, did not exist. It would become the first major engineering task.

Left: Like that of a dinosaur, the Vimy's great skeleton takes shape in a hangar at the abandoned air base at Hamilton Field, California. The crew put in fourteen-hour days and six-day weeks for more than a year to meet the ambitious schedule.

Above: Prop-maker Dick Sweetapple, of Brisbane, Australia, shows off the raw laminations he will shape into the 10-foot, 8-inch airscrews for the Vimy replica. The timber is Tasmanian oak. A finished propeller weighed in at 140 pounds.

Right: Designer Bill Whitney checks fuselage welds completed in Brisbane by Wayne Daley. Despite its massive size, the steel-tube fuselage frame was completed in three months and shipped gratis to the United States by Federal Express.

Making noise at Brisbane's Archerfield Airport, Dr. Peter Dueker operates the test-stand controls to obtain more information about the engine, gearbox and propeller. More than 75 hours of test runs were logged before this engine and prop were sent to the United States. They went the entire distance with the aircraft.

REDUCING THE REVS

Bill Whitney and Ted Baker, assisted by metallurgist Dr. Peter Dueker, designed a brilliantly compact 4:1 ratio epicyclic gearbox for the replica Vimy. Oil bath lubrication, heat-compensating bearings, double-face propeller drive and vacuum-cast aluminum casing, combined with quality-control limits in excess of those specified for Boeing 747 engines, resulted in a product with wide-ranging aviation, marine and industrial applications beyond the Vimy. A number of aviation organizations were surprised and impressed by the long-term reliability results of the gearboxes, which may go a long way to helping realize the dream of fitting inexpensive car engines to aircraft.

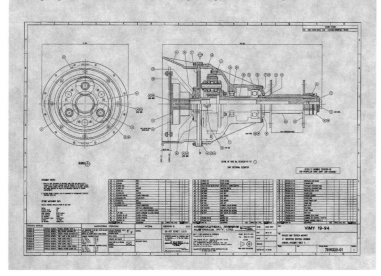

Above: The framework is laid out in Sonoma, California, before the pieces are moved to Hamilton Field. The rear fuselage is draped with the fabric from the original Vimy G-EAOU (loaned by Norman Pointing, of Adelaide, Australia).

We spared no expense, and the gearbox was built to space-shuttle standards in terms of metallurgy and tolerances. Pessimists from around the world proclaimed that our gearbox combination would fail, since the enormous torque created by the 4:1 reduction would create excessive heat and vibration, shaking the motor to bits or even tearing the centers out of the propellers. The cost of designing and constructing the gearbox came to more than $80,000. But even worse was the year of sleepless nights we suffered while we waited to find out whether the skeptics were wrong!

A GIANT PAPER AIRPLANE

Step two was for Bill Whitney to turn a few hundred 1918 blueprints from Brooklands into a set of working plans, complete with the mathematical justifications required to meet the standards of modern aircraft construction. More than 3,000 pages later, we found that, with very few exceptions, the Vickers engineers, with their slide rules, pencils and butcher's paper, had got the design as right as Bill could with his CAD (computer-aided design) system.

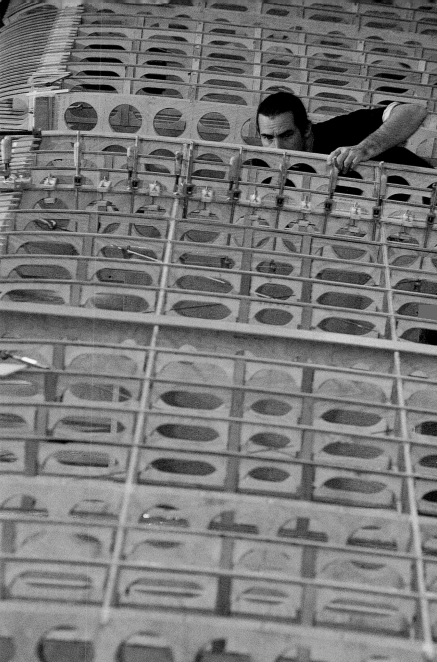

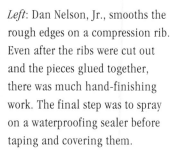

Left: Dan Nelson, Jr., smooths the rough edges on a compression rib. Even after the ribs were cut out and the pieces glued together, there was much hand-finishing work. The final step was to spray on a waterproofing sealer before taping and covering them.

Right: Standing between the unfinished wing panels, John La Noue sights the rib alignment. The wings had more than 80 standard ribs, 26 compression (double) ribs and more than 300 nose ribs to shape the leading edge. Some ribs were formed of more than 30 pieces.

The next step was to actually start construction. Early experience with the Australian Civil Aviation Authority convinced us that we had no choice but to assemble the aircraft in the United States, where regulations and bureaucracy are more progressive. It was essential, however, that the metal subassemblies, including the fuselage frame, fuel tanks, engines, gearboxes, and struts, be constructed in Australia, where Bill Whitney could keep a close eye on them. Accordingly, Wayne Daley, a Brisbane racing car builder, was contracted to take on these complex and varied tasks.

By April 1993, Wayne was hard at work bending metal. The first completed piece was a rudder, which we hoped would steer the project to success. The propellers also had to be made in Australia, close to where the engines and gearboxes were being built. Lang found a prop-maker, Dick Sweetapple, to carve up some sizable logs and shape them into two airscrews plus a spare.

SAWDUST SIERRAS
Meanwhile, in California, I asked John La Noue to consider dropping his career building sets and stage scenery for a year

or more. When this diehard perfectionist saw the incredible precision of Bill Whitney's drawings, he was hooked. An added bonus was that John brought in his partner, Dan Nelson, a master welder and fabricator. Dan would be inseparable from the Vimy until her last stop in Australia.

John studied numerous photographs of Brooklands in 1918, along with plans, manuals and construction regulations of the period. "We built a seventy-five-year-old airplane factory in Sonoma, California, from scratch," he once said. Renting a 10,000-foot warehouse in June, John, Dan and Dan Junior started producing mountains of sawdust…

The summer of '93 came, and we were in deep. We had two factories on opposite sides of the world and a design operation spewing out hundreds of pages of plans a week. Lang spent his time overseeing the various Australian subassemblies, as well as doing a great deal of historical research to further our quest for sponsorship. I was holding down my job in the investment business to keep the project afloat, as, inevitably, we were going through money faster than water through a bottomless bucket.

Above: Dan Nelson (left) and Wayne Daley adjust the thrust wires and engine mounts, which transmit the driving force of the propeller into the airframe. "If, when you thump it, she sounds like a bass guitar, that's about right," said Dan.

Left: The issue of *National Geographic* magazine for March 1921 featured Sir Ross Smith's personal account of his groundbreaking flight from London to Australia.

ROSS SMITH'S PUBLISHER

My friend John Owen offered generous funding from his company, Weldon Owen Publishing, but perhaps even more important, he introduced me to Mary Smith, a senior picture editor with *National Geographic* magazine. John and I convinced Mary of the seriousness of our endeavor, and she invited us to come back to Washington to meet the editor, Bill Graves.

It was our first hit after several misses. *National Geographic* magazine had published Ross Smith's personal account of his record-breaking flight in their March 1921 issue. The assistant editor for that issue was Ralph Graves, Bill's father. Bill and I first met in August 1993, and from our first luncheon it was clear that he would do everything in his power to make the Vimy fly. He accepted that there were great risks inherent in the project, but appreciated the fact that we were not cutting corners on engineering.

Bill invited National Geographic Television to come aboard. Their funding came as a great relief, but it also added to the pressure already on us to get the plane finished—and on time.

THE SPIRIT OF BROOKLANDS

Through the summer and fall of 1993, I was in England at least once a month for my job, and I made good use of my time over there looking for Vimy artifacts and researching anything related to the original flights at the London Science Museum, which has housed Alcock and Brown's transatlantic Vimy for seventy-five years. It was on one of these trips that I broadened my search to the Brooklands Museum, about 30 miles south of London.

Here I found tremendous enthusiasm for the project from Morag Barton, the fearless director of the young and growing museum, and from Julian Temple, the aviation curator. Far from being skeptical about our outrageous idea, Morag willingly made available to us her prestigious list of museum patrons who might be interested in supporting our project. She also arranged a special luncheon for potential sponsors in October 1993, attended by HRH Prince Michael of Kent, who graciously agreed to become the royal patron for the Vimy 19/94 project in response to a letter written on our behalf by Raymond Salisbury-Jones. The goodwill and credibility engendered by our association with

Left: Bev Kidby shows that the painstaking process of rib-stitching takes more than two hands.

Above: The hangar in California recalls the old days at Brooklands, except that all the fabric workers in the Vickers factory were women. The blankets of aircraft-grade cotton are spread out and then clamped into place until they are glued around the edges. Water-shrinking followed by two coats of nitrate dope will leave the curved wing surface drum-tight.

Right: John manhandles the prop into place. Once properly balanced, the huge fans produced surprisingly little excess vibration. There were good days and worse days, however, depending on the amount of water the wooden blades had soaked in.

Prince Michael and the Brooklands Museum helped immeasurably in our fund-raising efforts. In turn, I became inspired by the "spirit of Brooklands", and this place, which had many times seen success against long odds, became like a second home to me.

A CLOSE SHAVE

Through the summer and fall, the ship grew by leaps and bounds. We had yet to experience any serious problems in getting parts completed in the sequence necessary to keep the jobs rolling. Wayne Daley finished the 42-foot fuselage early in November, and Federal Express chairman Fred Smith (responding to a request from aviation author Walter Boyne) generously offered to airfreight it to California for us when the company had spare capacity. Lang left Australia with the fuselage, which required him to make the supreme sacrifice—his beard. There was a peculiar rule that beards were not permitted on these cargo flights, as they might interfere with using the oxygen system. Not only was Lang's face shorn, but he was obliged to spend a week at the Hong Kong YMCA waiting for space on one of

the daily cargo runs to California, having been bumped aside to make way for the pre-Christmas loads of teddy bears!

Lang came over to California for the duration, and his wife of twenty-five years, Bev, joined him at the Christmas holidays. We began to experience more ups and downs, since the Australian-made metal fittings needed to complete the wings couldn't be made fast enough. It was critical that we start work on the fabric wing covering, an extremely labor-intensive exercise, with more than 1,600 square feet of wing area to be covered. This was exacerbated by our decision, once again, to go the original way and use cotton rather than synthetic fabric. A team from AJD Engineering in the United Kingdom, builders of the world's most authentic World War I replicas, came across to show us the tricks of the covering trade using natural fabric.

AN IDEAL FACTORY

The winter was a roller coaster of success and failure, but our biggest victory came when, through Lang's persistence, we secured permission to move our main operation to Hamilton

Right: John sprays the final color coat on the tail section, while other workers finish lacing the unpainted fabric to the fuselage. Dan and Wayne continue the tedious process of installing the first engine.

Below: The forward section of the aircraft is taking shape. The wheel and flight controls are installed, and the very complex electrical system looks like so many strands of spaghetti. The levers between the seats are the throttles. The instruments and radios are still to come.

Above, right: Dan, Peter and John test-fit the left inner main wheel. The wheels were custom-made to the original dimensions at a cost of more than $12,000. Aircraft tires of this size and shape haven't been made for decades, but a set of farm equipment tires fit the wheels perfectly.

Right: An engineer at the Bruntons facility in Musselburgh, Scotland, threads one of the Vimy's streamlined wires through a cold rolling press. These bracing, or flying, wires carry the lift of the wings into the airframe, and therefore have to be individually tested, or "proof-loaded". The Vimy's wings are 10 feet apart, so many of the diagonal wires are over 14 feet long. The flying wires for the original G-EAOU were also made in this factory.

Field, in California. This generous gesture by the Defense Department and the Sixth United States Army gave us a 40,000-square-foot hangar and an ideal test-flying facility, since the airfield had been deactivated some years earlier and so there would be no competing traffic. The hangar had several smaller rooms that could be heated for fabric work—a process that is temperature-critical—and also an electric crane that could lift 7,000 pounds. This gantry crane helped prevent damage to the enormous wing sections as the workers moved them from the fabric room to the main floor. Almost as important was the fact that access to Hamilton was restricted, which gave us some privacy from the hundreds of curious well-wishers anxious to sneak a peek at the giant skeleton taking shape. Our ambitious schedule did not allow us to be cordial to the numerous unannounced guests who came by, but we did offer weekend tours of the facility.

MONEY MORE THAN WINGS

Despite the blessing of our free hangar, by the first quarter of 1994 it was clear that all the enthusiasm in the world wasn't going to keep me from going broke fairly soon. Labor and materials were costing more than $60,000 a month. Aluminum struts and fuel tanks had already set us back $85,000. We recruited some volunteers, including Bev Kidby, who proved to be an ace at fabric work, and my father, Tom, a retired physician, who turned his hand to every task, right down to cleaning the men's room in the hangar.

But we had to find money soon, or the whole project would grind to an ignominious halt. In February, I went to Bahrain to visit Shaikh Hamad bin Ebrahim Al Khalifa, who had expressed interest in the project through John Owen's Australian partner, Kevin Weldon. Shaikh Hamad quickly saw the possibility of mounting large-scale festivities centered on the Vimy to promote Bahrain, and not only offered generous funding himself but brought in the support of Gulf Air through the Minister for Development and Industry, His Excellency Yousuf A. Shirawi.

WE STILL NEED FUEL

We still needed a big corporate sponsor, and looked first to the two biggest sponsors of the 1919 flight, Shell and Kodak. Despite

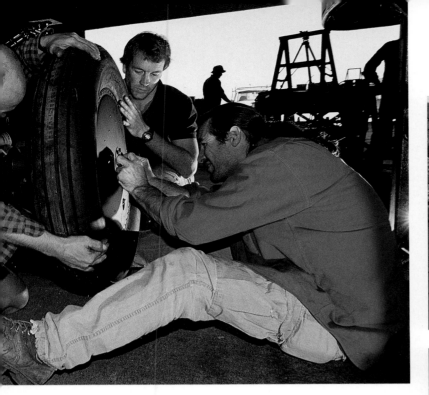

Above, right: The Vimy is rolled out for her first public viewing, at a party held on July 7, 1994, at the deactivated USAF base at Hamilton Field. A number of the project's patrons flew in for the occasion.

Right: Dan welds one of the axles, while other workers attend to the forward fuselage. Welding had to be done with care, given the close proximity of the flammable fabric wings.

the flight's significance as the first aerial survey of the world, our repeated efforts with Kodak failed to inspire them. Shell, on the other hand, welcomed us with open arms. A large sponsorship was arranged through the Shell International headquarters in London. The negotiations were handled by a motor-racing agent, Guy Edwards. Meeting Shell's needs along with those of National Geographic turned into a complex three-way affair, but, for the most part, both of our main sponsors were willing to work together in the altruistic spirit of the project.

There was still a great deal of financial juggling necessary, along with some substantial borrowings, but we had enough funding to get the Vimy into the air—just. Given their financial support, the sponsors naturally wanted some big events. Chief among these was to be our departure for Australia in September from the Farnborough Air Show, in the United Kingdom, with its week-long crowd of more than a million spectators. This put tremendous pressure on John, Wayne and Dan, since the plane was still looking fairly skeletal in May. Work on the cockpits and controls hadn't even begun. Even sixteen-hour days and seven-day weeks wouldn't get us to England in time, since it

would take a month to ship the mammoth airplane there. We needed another miracle.

A FIRST-CLASS TICKET, PLEASE

John Owen was acquainted with Don Lopez from the National Air and Space Museum, having previously produced a book with him. In June, Don offered to submit a request to the United States Air Force to give us a lift to England aboard a C-5 Galaxy transport plane—a huge advantage, allowing us to ship the Vimy in two big pieces. Lang, with the help of an Air Force official, John Ware, figured out a path through the Air Force maze via dozens of phone calls to the Pentagon. The pincer movement worked, and after a few dozen letters back and forth, the airlift was on, courtesy of the 439th Airlift Wing and the 337th Airlift Squadron from Westover, Massachusetts. They would even pick us up from Travis Air Force Base, which was only 30 miles from Hamilton! The catch was that our ticket was valid for only one day, August 23, 1994. That would allow for no major mistakes in the final assembly of the very complex fuel and electrical systems or even minor mishaps in fulfilling our 25-hour test-flying requirement.

Right: The guest of honor is brought before her first audience. A few parts are still to come, including the port engine, but spirits are high among all present. The master of ceremonies, Kevin Weldon, explained to the crowd that the missing engine was held by a local bank, pending more donations to retrieve it. Peter and Lang are wearing their newly arrived replica Sidcot No. 5 flying suits tailored by Gieves & Hawkes of London, makers of the suits worn by Ross and Keith Smith.

Left: The ample wing of the USAF allows the Vimy replica to hitch a ride to England aboard a C-5 Galaxy from Travis Air Force Base, in California. The airlift was provided by the 439th Airlift Wing and the 337th Airlift Squadron, based in Westover, Massachusetts. By their standards, the cargo was very light, weighing in at just under 10,000 pounds.

Right: Latitude 33°51'S, longitude 151°13'E
The Vimy glides past Sydney Harbour Bridge and the unmistakable Opera House. Good fortune has prevailed. Despite the hurdles, she has lumbered almost 14,000 miles from England.

Our frenetic pace made it necessary to outsource more and more of the subassemblies to local Californian firms, which led to some costly mistakes. We rarely had problems with parts built on site. Wayne arrived in July to install the engines, now that the wings had been rigged. Our test engine had run for 75 hours with no problem. The gearbox was vindicated! We all took a breather for a glorious roll-out party on July 7.

HITTING THE LIMELIGHT

Several hundred well-dressed patrons were stunned as they saw the huge green aircraft roll out through the doors. They would have been even more stunned had they known that the wheels had been fitted only an hour earlier! It was a proud moment in all of our lives. From people's reaction, it was evident that the sight of our unlikely flying machine had rekindled a long-lost sense of adventure and optimism. Not the least adventurous were the people from the aviation insurance organization USAIG, which provided hull coverage for the Vimy.

It was all or nothing now, and time to quit my job of the last eleven years. Taking three private planes on a trip through nineteen countries involves more than a little planning in terms of such things as fuel, flight and immigration clearances. Mark Rebholz stepped in to handle the clearances and flight planning, while Tessa Barroll and I took care of the reams of correspondence alerting more than fifty embassies to our plans and generating publicity for Shell and the other sponsors, along with some last-minute fund-raising. Meanwhile, John, Wayne and Lang tried to organize all the contractors producing the subassemblies for the multitude of items that had to be brought together in the right order—rather like orchestrating a fifty-course French dinner.

July 30 was the big day. After several trials taxiing down the runway and hours of engine runs, Peter Hoar, a veteran of the 1969 Vimy project, took the controls, with Lang beside him in the right-hand seat. The Vimy broke free of the ground at 1919 hours (by sheer good luck), and stayed aloft for eleven minutes. A fuel injector problem then forced her down, but the plane had

handled like a dream. The celebration we held that night in our huge, ghost-town-like air force base echoed into the early hours.

SCHIZOPHRENIC PEGASUS

I took the controls for the first time on August 2. Although acutely aware that I could, in a second, destroy 20,000 man-hours of labor, I was enjoying myself after only a few minutes. Of the many antique planes I have flown, the Vimy was by far the heaviest and most sluggish, but you simply had to nudge her hard, like an old mare. After a few more flights, I learned that our gentle old mare turned into a nasty, bucking stallion when the air became turbulent.

Over the next three weeks, we flew our required 25 hours with only a few incidents. Del Ott of the Federal Aviation Administration, our friend and adviser since the beginning, gave us our official registration, NX-7IMY, on August 18. With his permission, we had painted the letters G-EAOU across the wings and fuselage in homage to our predecessors.

We flew her to Travis on August 20. A few days later, the Vimy was disassembled and stuffed down the throat of a C-5 Galaxy, and we were all aboard, bound for England. Unbelievable. I was sitting in the Vimy's cockpit 30,000 feet above the Atlantic.

HERE'S TO THE RISK-TAKERS

The task of coordinating and responding to the needs of the hundreds of different people and groups who were involved in the project, financially and otherwise, was indescribably complex. But there was never a dull moment, and dozens of times, the failure of one person on one day could have brought the project down. Corporate lawyers, insurance providers, government regulators and military officials: it is often said that such people are hopelessly conservative and unimaginative, yet many of these professionals took on great risks for themselves and their organizations for the greater goal of getting the Vimy into the air and safely from England to Australia. A modern miracle? Hardly—the spirit of adventure is alive and well around the world.

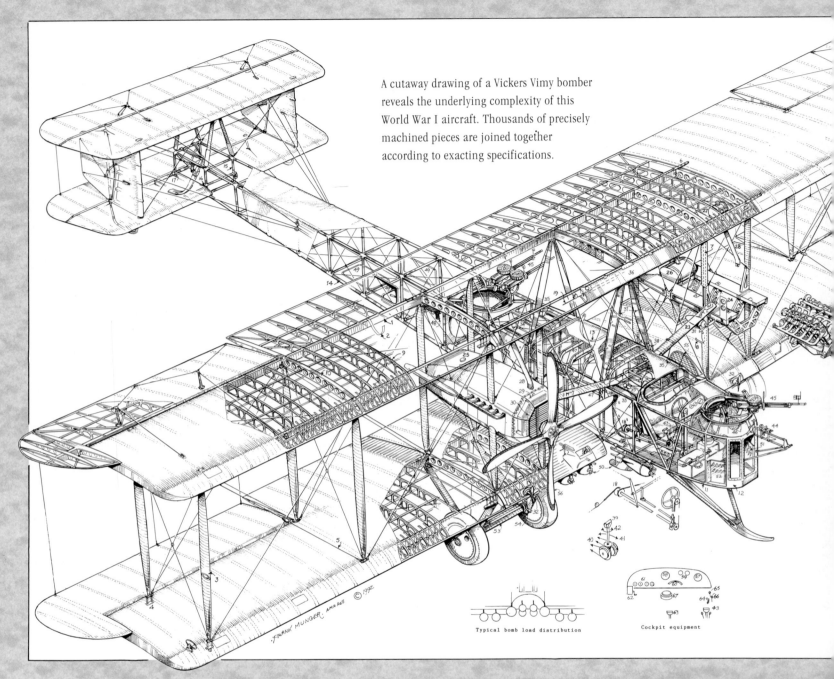

A cutaway drawing of a Vickers Vimy bomber reveals the underlying complexity of this World War I aircraft. Thousands of precisely machined pieces are joined together according to exacting specifications.

FRANK MUNGER AMRAeS ©1992

Typical bomb load distribution   Cockpit equipment

SOME MAJOR FEATURES

1. Spruce and plywood box spars
3. Hollow spruce struts
5. Lift wires (heavier gauge than landing wires)
7. Steel-tube engine-bearing struts
9. Ply and spruce ribs
10. Box-section compression ribs
20. Aileron control pulleys
21. Cables to port and starboard rudders
22. 360-h.p. Rolls Royce Eagle VIII engine
24. Engine RPM and temperature gauges
34. Aft fuel tank (140 gallons)
54. Rubber bungee shock absorber
55. Propeller guard (starboard side omitted)
56. Vickers propeller (10 ft. 6 in. diameter)

Right: A graceful curved bow made of fourteen layers of birch aircraft plywood forms the leading-edge wing-tip. The bow was free-form-laminated, using a vacuum-bag process.

Opposite page: John La Noue, Chief Engineer for the Vimy project, contemplates the arrangement of the nose gunner's cockpit. "Building the Vimy was an exercise in creative problem-solving," said John. "Every day we experienced unique problems that had not been encountered for seventy-five years."

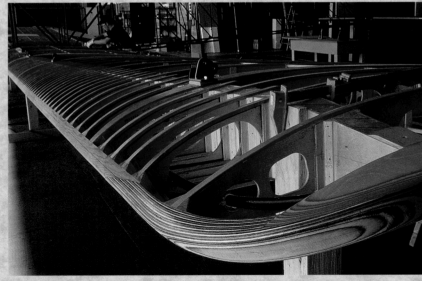

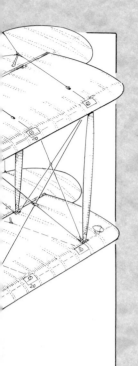

BUILDING THE VIMY

NOW THAT'S A CHALLENGE. Those were my first words after being offered the job of building what would become the largest flying replica aircraft in the world. My excitement at such an undertaking was outshone only by the infectious enthusiasm of the person making the offer, a young man named Peter McMillan. To see and hear Peter talk of recreating one of the world's most magnificent and historically significant aircraft was to realize I was in the presence of a true believer, one who still possessed the kind of faith it would take to move the mountains of obstacles on the path to recreating the Vimy. I knew then that faith was a prerequisite to accepting his offer. Some of the highlights of the year that followed are recounted here.

BLUEPRINTS FOR A DINOSAUR

"Here's your bedtime reading for this weekend. Guaranteed insomnia!" Peter said, handing me the first stack of preliminary drawings. It was my first encounter with Bill Whitney of Aeronautical Designs Australia. And my first look at the fastidiously accurate and detailed

drawings that would consume my life for the next year. Bill was our aeronautical engineer for the project and was in charge of all design work and stress analysis. Over the course of constructing the Vimy, I came to appreciate the fine quality of his work and his incredible attention to detail.

My first impression as I studied the wing drawings spread out before me was that neither the design nor the construction method was particularly complex. But as I began to comprehend the Vimy's dimensions, the scale of the project became alarmingly apparent. For the wings and ailerons alone, 330 feet of box spar would have to be fabricated. The volume of materials required was staggering, and I knew we would need to secure the necessary quantities immediately if we were to meet our schedule.

WINGS FROM THE FOREST

Back in the days when aircraft were still made of wood and fabric, the timber of choice was Sitka Spruce, a tree indigenous to a small strip of land along the northern Pacific coast of

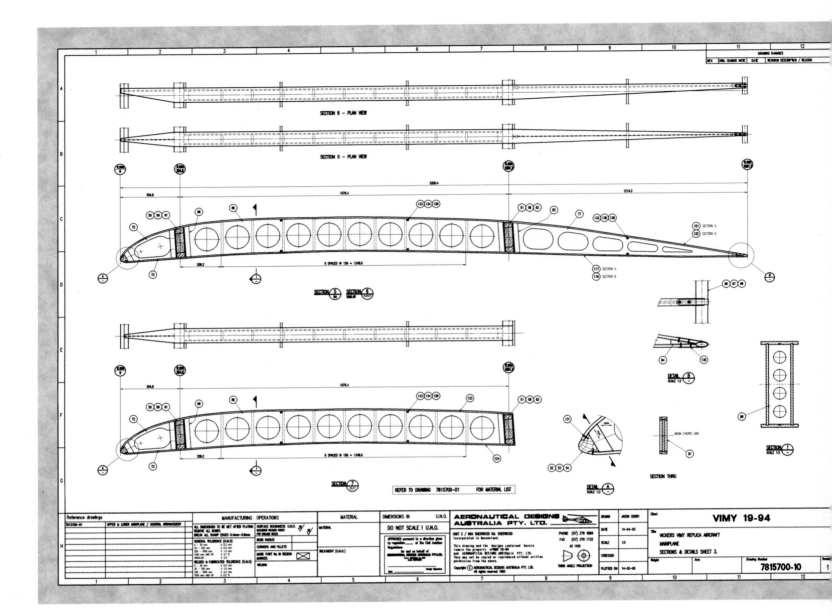

North America. Sitka Spruce is ideal for aircraft construction because of its strength to weight ratio. But with so little demand for aircraft-grade Sitka Spruce nowadays, supplies are limited. We therefore had to find a more readily available alternative.

Fortunately, California has vast forests of Douglas Fir trees. This timber is 18 percent heavier than Sitka Spruce but also 16 percent stronger, and is approved for use in aircraft construction by the Federal Aviation Administration. Bill Whitney was willing to accept its increased weight as a tradeoff against its greater strength, which would add a slight margin of safety.

A VOLUME OF FORGOTTEN LORE

Since there are no longer any lumber mills specializing in timber for aircraft use, I had to painstakingly select several thousand board feet of Douglas Fir from the available commercial sources. The wood was then subjected to a rigorous in-house inspection and testing program based on criteria laid down in a 330-page publication issued by the government in 1944 called *Army Navy Civil Bulletin #19: Wood Aircraft Inspection and Fabrication*.

ANC #19 became my bible, and selecting lumber was undoubtedly one of the most tedious and time-consuming tasks in the early construction stages. The wood had to be inspected for moisture content, grain slope, specific gravity and annual ring count, and to be free of such defects as knots, spiral grain, worm holes, compression wood, compression failure, pitch pockets, bark pockets, shake, splits, checks, dote, rot and so on. More than 100 sheets of birch aircraft plywood were also required, primarily for spar webs, wing ribs and empennage ribs. Fortunately, even though it had to come all the way from Finland, aircraft plywood is readily available.

BUILDING A FACTORY

Many times during the process of building this World War I replica, I would think about how those early craftsmen at the Vickers factory at Brooklands might have fabricated the same bits and pieces I was now responsible for creating. It still amazes me when I look at the finished aircraft to recall that a good 40 percent of the work was not even part of the aircraft itself.

Opposite page: The contemporary blueprint for a compression rib.

Far left: Every piece of wood that came into the shop had to be dated, graded and batch-stamped.

Left, top: An aileron cable pulley attached to the forward spar.

Left: Final milling on one of the Vimy's box-spar frames.

Below: Dan and John apply glue to the wing ribs.

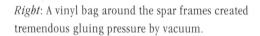

Above: John La Noue displays an aluminum rib template (*left*). Dan Nelson demonstrates how the templates are used to rout rib sections out of plywood (*right*).

Right: A vinyl bag around the spar frames created tremendous gluing pressure by vacuum.

Left: The spar components: plywood spar web, on front and back side; laminated spar cap, top and bottom; solid compression block.

Below: A side view of the forward spar with the nose ribs attached.

It is no exaggeration to say that before we could build the airplane, we had to build the factory and fabricate many of our own parts—all the jigs, fixtures, molds and special tooling. Although we did not have Vickers' resources and manpower, we had seventy years of technological improvement on our side. Time and money were the forces that shaped our construction methods. Since both were limited, we developed an almost Zen-like approach to our work: Do it once, do it right, no wasted motion, and absolutely no going backwards.

CONSTRUCTING THE SPARS

One of the first steps in building the Vimy's wings was fabricating the wing spars. These are the main load-bearing structures that run parallel to the lateral axis of the aircraft. The spars are truly the foundation of the airplane, for they support the entire load of the aircraft in flight. The Vimy's design calls for a type of spar known as a box spar, which is essentially a long, hollow wooden box made up of spar caps, spar webs and compression blocks (see illustration).

Left and below: The firehose press provided even pressure of up to 100 psi. Dan Nelson removes spar cap laminations after the glue has set.

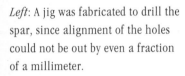

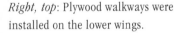

Left: A jig was fabricated to drill the spar, since alignment of the holes could not be out by even a fraction of a millimeter.

Right, top: Plywood walkways were installed on the lower wings.

Right: A 15:1 angle is required for scarf joints (sections glued together).

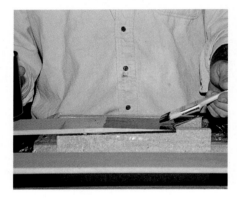

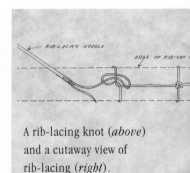

A rib-lacing knot (*above*) and a cutaway view of rib-lacing (*right*).

The compression blocks were glued between the two spar caps to form a framework measuring approximately 1 9/16 inches by 6 1/2 inches in cross section and between 8 and 21 feet in length, depending on whether they were to be used in a lower center-section spar, an aileron, an upper center-section spar or an outer-wing spar. The frame was then enclosed by gluing a spar web to each side, forming a lightweight structure of incredible strength.

To fabricate the spars, I found it necessary to build two pieces of specialized equipment: a pneumatic press for laminating the spar caps, and a vacuum press for gluing the plywood spar webs to the frames.

FIREHOSE PRESS

The pneumatic press consisted of a 24-foot-long framework of square steel tubing with two parallel 5-inch-high fences of square steel tube extending the length of its top surface. Eight strips, or "laminae", of 4-inch-wide Douglas Fir, scarf-jointed to a length of 24 feet, were coated with glue, placed in stacks of four into each side of the huge press, and then squeezed by inflating a firehose running down the middle of the framework.

After curing in the press, the now-laminated lengths of Douglas Fir were sawn in half lengthwise, since the Vimy's

spars were about 2 inches wide. Several more milling and finishing operations followed, and the spar caps were then assembled into frames, ready for the webs to be glued on.

VACUUM TABLE

The function of the vacuum press was to provide even clamping pressure for gluing the webs, or "skins", to the frames. It consisted of a very smooth and precisely leveled table 12 inches wide by 24 feet long, with plastic tubes connected to a rotary-vane vacuum pump plumbed into its surface. The web and frame interfaces were coated with wet glue, joined together, and placed on the table. A thick, clear vinyl sheet was placed on top and sealed to the table with special tape. The vacuum pump was then activated, removing all air from the "bag" and creating a vacuum of approximately 25 inches of mercury—equivalent to 11 tons of atmospheric pressure bearing down evenly upon the surface.

WE NEEDED A COTTON PLANTATION

"Five hundred yards! Wow!" It was hard to believe. I recalculated my figures, and it was going to take almost 500 yards of airwing-grade cotton fabric to cover the aircraft and to make the surface tapes. There was nothing small about

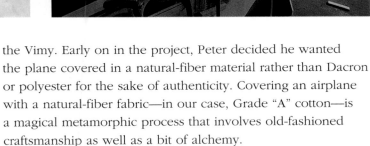

Left, top: Because of the curvature of the leading edge, nose-rib caps had to be glued and steamed in a jig.

Left, center: Stacks of finished nose ribs. More than 300 were installed.

Left, below: Caps were glued to the compression ribs with C-clamps. Struts and wires were bolted on.

Below: A fabric blanket is spread across the underside of a wing section (here, upside down). To prevent chafing, medical tape was applied to all surfaces in contact with the fabric skin. The concave underside of the Vimy's wings is visible. This primitive airfoil shape is inefficient, but was recreated for accuracy.

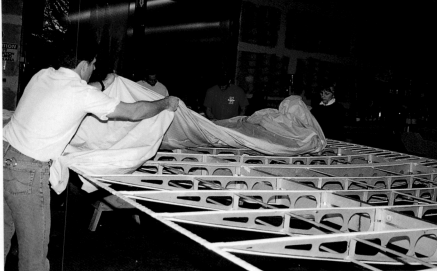

the Vimy. Early on in the project, Peter decided he wanted the plane covered in a natural-fiber material rather than Dacron or polyester for the sake of authenticity. Covering an airplane with a natural-fiber fabric—in our case, Grade "A" cotton—is a magical metamorphic process that involves old-fashioned craftsmanship as well as a bit of alchemy.

In the process of covering the Vimy, the logistics of size were always a major factor. Dealing with acres of fabric, hundreds of gallons of dope and thinner, and large sections of airframe presented a challenge that forced us to come up with clever solutions. The first task was to devise a means of gaining easy access to both sides of the wing panel. This would have been no problem if we had been dealing with the wings of a conventional-size rag-wing airplane, but it was going to be extremely difficult to manually rotate wing panels weighing several hundred pounds. And the massive panels could easily be damaged in the process. To overcome this problem, I decided to build a giant "rotisserie".

QUEEN-SIZE BLANKETS

The Grade "A" cotton airwing fabric was manufactured in bolts measuring 60 inches wide by 100 yards long. To form a blanket to cover a wing panel such as the upper center section,

five 22-foot lengths of fabric would have to be sewn edge to edge. The blanket had to be big enough to envelop the entire wing, stretching from the trailing edge, over the top surface, around the leading edge, and back under the bottom surface, returning to the trailing edge.

Excess fabric was then trimmed off, and the fabric edges were glued to the trailing edge and the compression ribs at each end of the wing panel with special fabric cement. The "skin" was now ready to be shrunk. By means of a paint spray-gun, the cotton surface was lightly misted with distilled water. Within minutes, the skin became drum-tight, a snap of the finger producing deep reverberations. When completely dry, the skin was ready for its first coat of dope.

SKIN-TIGHT

Dope is a type of heavy-bodied lacquer that is applied to the fabric to provide a weatherproof, plastic-like finish that is both tough and durable. Nitrocellulose, or "nitrate", dope was used exclusively for the primary and fill coats, and butyrate dope for the silver and color coats. The dope was brushed onto the fabric as much as possible rather than sprayed, which is the more common practice nowadays. Brushing was used in the early days and gave the aircraft of that era a distinctive look,

Above: A wing section is spun on the "rotisserie", allowing the workers to seal the envelope of cotton around the massive frame.

Left, top: Internal hardware and bracing wires are installed. Copper bonding tape and cloth tape are then applied before covering.

Left, center: Fabric is glued to the edge of the frame.

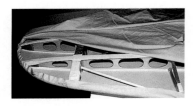

Left: After covering, hand-frayed tapes are applied over all ribs.

the brush strokes being visible in the surface finish. The work environment was also better without the clouds of noxious overspray. Brushing has the additional advantage of being relatively quick: two people can brush a coat on both sides of a panel in about half an hour.

For the first coat, the solution was thinned to ensure good penetration into the fabric. As it dried out, the fabric would slacken, and after the second coat, the wing surface would look downright awful, not unlike a very wet paper bag. To the uninitiated, it looked as though something had gone very wrong and that it might be time to rip off all the fabric and start over. In fact, this was a natural stage in the metamorphic covering process. After the third coat, the fabric skin would start to shrink once again and regain its former tautness.

TEN THOUSAND STITCHES

Rib-lacing, or rib-stitching, is what holds the fabric to the ribs. Without it, airflow over the wing would cause the fabric to balloon up, distorting the airfoil shape and resulting in a loss of lift.

Preparatory to stitching, a strip of selfadhesive polyester herringbone tape was placed along the sections of fabric covering the top and bottom rib caps. This acts as reinforcement and prevents the stitching cord from tearing the lightweight fabric.

So-called "centers" were then marked with a pencil along the length of each rib, on both the top and bottom surfaces, to indicate where each rib-stitch knot would be tied. The distance between the centers on different parts of the wing panel was determined by a formula based on the variable factors of wing loading, maximum speed and whether the area would be subject to the force of the propeller's slipstream. The rib stitches in the propeller slipstream were only 1 1/2 inches apart, while those outside the slipstream were 3 inches apart.

We were now ready to start stitching. Since the Vimy's wings and flying surfaces would require more than 10,000 knots to be tied with waxed cord (with a breaking strength of 80 pounds), I decided to go with the most basic version: a surface-tied, modified seine knot. This was also one of the easiest knots to learn—an advantage when we were depending for the most part on a crew of volunteers to do this tedious and time-consuming task.

Tying the knots with the right amount of tension required practice. It took several days to stitch the first panel. But soon, with a little experience under their belt, several teams of stitchers could tie the 900 to 1,000 knots in each full-size wing panel in about twelve hours. Altogether, 4 outer wing panels, 1 upper center wing panel, 2 lower center-section wing panels,

Left: Seamstress Jane Lucas sits on a ladder during a test-fit of the fuselage fabric she sewed. Grommets were hammered into the borders of the fuselage panels to allow them to be laced together with a "baseball" stitch. The fabric was easily removable, like the original.

Below: Nitrate dope is brushed on a wing panel mounted on the rotisserie. Workers wear masks to protect them from the noxious fumes. Brushing is not only more environmentally sensitive than spraying, but also gives the fabric surface a more original look.

Left: Distilled water is sprayed over the covered wing panel to initiate the shrinking process. After the wing dries, the initial coat of nitrate, or clear, dope can be applied.

Below: Most wing ribs required 84 laces: three hours of knot-tying even for a dexterous stitcher.

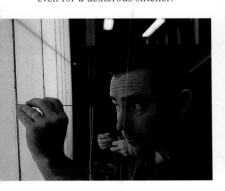

4 ailerons, 1 upper horizontal stabilizer, 2 lower horizontal stabilizers, 2 vertical stabilizers, 2 elevators and 2 rudders had to be rib-stitched after two coats of clear dope had been applied.

A MILE OF TAPES

The next step was to apply the surface tapes, which provide an additional layer of fabric reinforcement. At the old Vickers factory, fabric workers made their own tapes by tearing off strips of fabric of the desired width and then stripping warp threads from the edges to leave a frayed edge. This edge was a distinctive feature of the aircraft of that era. Although modern, machine-cut, pinked-edge tapes achieve the same effect, they look noticeably different, so, despite the extra labor, we decided to stick to the traditional method.

For weeks before, we ripped, frayed, ironed and then carefully hung hundreds of strips of cotton tapes. Starting at the leading edge, a surface tape measuring 11 feet long by 2 1/4 inches wide was pressed onto the wet dope and smoothed down onto the underlying fabric, covering the exposed rib stitches all the way to the trailing edge. Dope was then applied to the top surface of the tape and brushed to feather out the frayed edges of the tape so that they adhered to the underlying fabric.

HIGH-ALTITUDE SUNSCREEN

At this point, the entire wing panel was covered with nitrate dope and allowed to dry. This process was repeated until there was sufficient buildup to provide a smooth satin gloss finish without obscuring the fabric weave. A total of six coats was usually required, including the three coats applied before rib-stitching. Next, two coats of silver dope were applied as a protective barrier against ultraviolet light, which causes cotton to deteriorate very quickly. Finally, two coats of green butyrate dope were applied, carefully matched to fabric swatches from the original G-EAOU, which had been loaned to us by Norman Pointing, of Adelaide, South Australia.

RIGGING THE WINGS

It had been years since anyone in the world had rigged the wings of a biplane of this size, so there was no pool of common knowledge to draw from. There were a lot of experts familiar with such airplanes as the Boeing Stearman and the Waco to offer advice, but with her huge wings, the Vimy required innovative methods.

Before the fabric was fitted and the dope applied, the three upper-wing panels and their ailerons had been placed on low sawhorses and assembled together to check the fit of all the

Above: Installing the right engine. This was the easy part: it would take a month of wiring and plumbing before the engine barked to life.

Below: The team gathers in front of the emerging Vimy replica. From left: Wayne Daley, Lang Kidby, Peter McMillan, John La Noue, Dan Nelson.

Above: Installing the upper wing. This innovative method required a truss (visible above the upper wing) normally used for lifting stage scenery or curtains. Geometry was critical, so the truss was connected to the wing by precisely made steel brackets to keep it level tip to tip and tilted backwards at an angle of 3 degrees.

hardware and control cables. During this dry fit-up, it became obvious that the size and weight of the wing panels, combined with the close tolerances between bolts, connecting plates, bolt holes and hinges—many of them awkward to get at—were going to make the job quite hard enough without the acrobatics of doing it 16 feet in the air.

Old photographs from the Vickers factory show that the early Vimys' lower center-section wing panels were bolted to the fuselage first, followed by the cabane struts, the engine struts, the upper center-section wing panel, associated bracing wires and the undercarriage. The outer lower-wing panels, outer upper-wing panels, ailerons, and associated struts and bracing wires were fitted at a later date. This allowed more aircraft to be housed inside the factory while such processes as engine installation were completed. But this two-step approach to assembly and rigging was not efficient enough for our small operation. It seemed to me that if we could assemble all three upper-wing panels with ailerons on and then attach them to the rest of the airplane, we would be saving a lot of work.

THREE FOR THE PRICE OF ONE

When assembled as a unit with their struts and bracing wires, the upper and lower wings form an extremely strong unit. By itself, however, the upper wing is not strong enough to withstand being lifted as one piece without substantial support. It needed to be lifted at many points while being supported by another structure along its 68-foot length. For the support structure, I decided to use the type of lightweight aluminum truss used for hanging lighting and scenery in stage productions. Several lengths of this truss could be joined to form the required length.

First, the upper-wing panels were joined together on the ground with both ailerons and aileron balance cable installed. The entire unit was supported by special jack stands, which held the upper-wing assembly at the correct angle of dihedral and angle of incidence. (Dihedral refers to the angle between the tips and root of the wing. The outer-wing panels of the Vimy angled upwards 3 degrees from their root.)

THE CRITICAL ANGLES

The next step was to devise a way of attaching the truss to the upper wing. Seven 5-foot-long steel bars made from 2-inch-square tube were placed across the fore and aft spars, the dimensions of each bar being calculated according to the angle of dihedral and angle of incidence required to position the bar correctly on the wing. The result was seven parallel

The pilot's cockpit is taking shape. The control wheel and column are installed; the yellow object at lower right is the fuel selector box.

Dan Nelson checks out the engine mounts, which must bear the weight and vibration of the 600-pound V-8 motor.

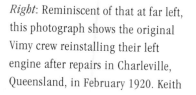

Right: Reminiscent of that at far left, this photograph shows the original Vimy crew reinstalling their left engine after repairs in Charleville, Queensland, in February 1920. Keith Smith, in the pith helmet, holds the hoisting chain, while Ross steadies the motor with his left hand on the gearbox. Jim Bennett and Wally Shiers are up on the wing.

bars aligned in a perfectly level plane spread out along and slightly above the wing, providing a platform from which the truss could be attached. The aluminum truss was then suspended from the hook of the rolling overhead gantry crane by a five-point bridle of steel cable, lowered onto the steel bars spanning the fore and aft spars, and fastened with nylon slings and shackles. The upper wing was now ready for rigging to the lower wing and fuselage.

The lower wing and fuselage were similarly prepared before being rigged together with the upper wing. To support the fuselage and lower wing, special adjustable steel jack stands were constructed. Supported by these stands, the fuselage was leveled and the lower wings attached to it. With the aid of the transit and some trigonometric calculations, the lower wing tips could then be brought to rest at their proper angle of dihedral by adjusting the jack screws.

AN UNSCHEDULED FLIGHT

Tipping the scales at almost 1,000 pounds, the Vimy's completed 68-foot upper wing took its first flight 18 feet above the ground unattached to the rest of the airplane. It was being lifted and propelled by the rolling overhead gantry crane in Hangar 86 at Hamilton Air Force Base, in Novato, California,

the site where the aircraft was assembled. As I stood at the electric crane controls, carefully maneuvering the wing to its correct position above the lower wing and fuselage, I was acutely aware of all that could go wrong: a broken weld or a poorly swaged cable, and six months of hard work would come crashing to the ground. The wing caught a momentary breeze of early morning air coming through the wide-open hangar doors, briefly giving the illusion of flight.

"Stop!" shouted a voice ringing with alarm. I quickly released the lateral control button, expecting to hear the sound of tearing fabric and snapping wood. The wing began to rock precariously back and forth. The four men on the tag lines at each end of the wing pulled hard on their ropes in an effort to keep 700 square feet of wing from swaying out of control. The premature stop had left the wing 18 inches short of its destination.

I looked across to my foreman, Dan Nelson, one of two men standing on plywood platforms that spanned the motor mounts between the engine struts. Dan was biting his tongue as he glared at the overanxious alarmist. He didn't like his authority being overridden by the inexperienced.

"OK, John, just a couple of bumps more. Easy." I gave the lateral control button a short burst. "Easy, easy now." The boys

between the engine struts could now guide the wing into position by hand. Gently, I began to lower the crane hook.

"Coming down slow, coming down easy. Stop!" shouted Dan. The top clevis ends of the engine struts were now wiggled onto their attach lugs on the underside of the upper wing with the aid of drift pins. It was time for high fives as we all breathed sighs of relief.

STRENGTH FROM SCOTLAND

Installing the four cabane struts and the eight remaining interplane struts came next. The cabane struts form a triangle with the fuselage and, when in place, automatically center the upper wing laterally. It was then time to fit the external streamlined bracing wires, specially manufactured for us by Bruntons of Musselburgh, in Scotland, who made the wires for the original Vimys seventy-five years ago. Their job is to hold the leading edge of the upper wing in its proper relationship to that of the lower wing. Weighted string lines were attached to the leading edge of the upper wing and allowed to hang below that of the lower wing. Tension was then gradually applied to the drag and antidrag wires until the string line just kissed the leading edge of the lower wing. This showed that the wings were aligned correctly.

The landing wires were the next to be adjusted, tension being applied until the wing had just started to float off the jack stands supporting the lower wing. It then remained to adjust the flying wires, which support the wings while in flight, when positive lift is being generated by the airfoil. Just enough tension was applied to these wires to produce a distinctive, bass-like sound when they were plucked like a bow string. Tensioning the bracing wires was not unlike tuning a large musical instrument. Too much tension on wires would preload the structure and produce higher bass notes when the wires were plucked. The entire process of rigging the main wing was completed in two days.

COUNTDOWN TO VICTORY

The Vimy rolled out of the hangar with the ponderous gait of a prehistoric beast and began to traverse the acres of empty tarmac toward the runway of our abandoned air force base. A collection of pickup trucks and automobiles filled with Vimy building crew and volunteers followed in friendly pursuit to take up positions along the edge of the runway. A small crowd of Vimy groupies who had been gathering every day for the last week in anticipation of a surprise first flight ran ragtag behind the plane with cameras in hand.

Opposite page: Victory! The Vimy's successful first test flight was an inspiration to all who had labored so long and so hard to create her.

Left: The wing structure of the Vimy enters the jaws of the colossal USAF C-5 Galaxy in preparation for transport to the United Kingdom.

Below: The flags of three nations bear testimony to the international effort required to recreate the machine that made global travel a reality.

In the right seat of the cockpit was Lang Kidby, acting as copilot. In the left seat, at the controls and acting as pilot-in-command, sat Peter Hoar, our test pilot from the United Kingdom. Without a doubt, Peter was the calmest and most relaxed person I had ever met. Without a sign of trepidation, he went about the business of testing this unproven aircraft in typically polite British fashion. His plan for today was to make a few high-speed taxi runs to test the responsiveness of the rudders, tailwheel and brakes.

I was about to join this unusual procession when I realized that, in the excitement, fire extinguishers and other safety equipment had not been loaded onto the escort vehicles. I rushed back into the hangar and began loading them onto my pickup truck.

"WE DID IT!"

Although I couldn't see the first ray of sunshine ever to appear beneath the Vimy's wheels, I heard the shouts of those who could. The plane was soon silhouetted against a sea of blue sky. The signature registration G-EAOU had not yet been painted on her wings, and she looked like a monstrous black dragonfly droning its way toward the heavens late on that summer afternoon, July 30, 1994.

I suddenly became aware of the oddest thing. I was completely alone, enjoying an incredible personal triumph in complete solitude. Slowly I began to walk toward the Vimy faithful who were still standing on the runway screaming and shouting with joy. It was a moment to be enjoyed one step at a time. As I walked across the barren tarmac, I let my mind reflect on all that had been accomplished in the year since we began the overwhelming task of shaping huge quantities of raw materials into the millions of pieces needed to produce a finished, functional flying machine. Words will never adequately describe the unfaltering dedication and perfectionism of those who worked endless hours to bring about what is usually thought to be the common and ordinary spectacle of an airplane in flight.

As I approached the runway, I could see the tears, the joy and the relief of those who had witnessed the fulfillment of what we had set out to achieve. But despite the celebration on the ground and the miracle in the sky, the finest sight had to be that of a man who had dared to turn a dream into reality enjoying a moment of pure exaltation. At that moment, Peter McMillan, who had put his faith in and bet a fortune on the abilities of me and my fellow craftsmen, turned to me with the widest of grins and said, "We did it!"

FLIGHT LOG: 1919

Date	Route	Time	Distance (miles)
12 Nov.	London–Lyons	6 hr. 20 min.	500
13 Nov.	Lyons–Pisa	4 hr. 45 min.	380
15 Nov.	Pisa–Rome	3 hr. 20 min.	180
16 Nov.	Rome–Taranto	2 hr. 35 min.	260
17 Nov.	Taranto–Suda Bay (Crete)	5 hr. 40 min.	520
18 Nov.	Suda Bay–Cairo	7 hr. 20 min.	650
19 Nov.	Cairo–Damascus	4 hr. 10 min.	450
20 Nov.	Damascus–Ramadie	6 hr.	420
21 Nov.	Ramadie–Basra	3 hr. 30 min.	350
23 Nov.	Basra–Bundar Abbas	7 hr. 40 min.	630
24 Nov.	Bundar Abbas–Karachi	8 hr. 30 min.	730
25 Nov.	Karachi–Delhi	9 hr.	720
27 Nov.	Delhi–Allahabad	4 hr. 25 min.	380
28 Nov.	Allahabad–Calcutta	5 hr.	470
29 Nov.	Calcutta–Akyab (Burma)	4 hr. 45 min.	420
30 Nov.	Akyab–Rangoon	4 hr. 15 min.	330
1 Dec.	Rangoon–Bangkok	6 hr.	400
2 Dec.	Bangkok–Singora	6 hr.	470
4 Dec.	Singora–Singapore	6 hr. 20 min.	480
6 Dec.	Singapore–Kalidjati (Java)	9 hr.	640
7 Dec.	Kalidjati–Surabaya	4 hr. 20 min.	350
8 Dec.	Surabaya–Bima (Sumbawa)	5 hr.	420
9 Dec.	Bima–Atamboea (Timor)	5 hr. 30 min.	440
10 Dec.	Atamboea–Port Darwin (Aust.)	6 hr. 30 min.	470
Total		**135 hr. 55 min.**	**11,060**

FLIGHT LOG: 1994

Date	Route	Time	Distance (miles)
11 Sept.	Farnborough–Troyes	3 hr. 39 min.	338
12 Sept.	Troyes–Chalon-sur-Saône	1 hr. 55 min.	123
12 Sept.	Chalon-sur-Saône–Lyon	1 hr. 14 min.	72
12 Sept.	Lyon–Benoux (Mende)	2 hr. 3 min.	115
13 Sept.	Mende–Cannes	2 hr. 48 min.	191
13 Sept.	Cannes–Pisa	3 hr. 2 min.	189
14 Sept.	Pisa, local (aborted)	29 min.	
15 Sept.	Pisa–Rome	2 hr. 40 min.	178
15 Sept.	Rome–Taranto	3 hr. 28 min.	302
16 Sept.	Taranto–Brindisi	21 min.	28
16 Sept.	Brindisi–Athens	4 hr. 2 min.	379
17 Sept.	Athens–Soúda Bay (Crete)	3 hr. 30 min.	183
18 Sept.	Soúda Bay–Alexandria	5 hr. 10 min.	463
18 Sept.	Alexandria–Cairo (Embaba)	1 hr. 20 min.	106
19 Sept.	Embaba, local (pyramids)	1 hr. 18 min.	
20 Sept.	Embaba–Cairo International	16 min.	
21 Sept.	Cairo–Ha'il	9 hr. 39 min.	742
22 Sept.	Ha'il–Bahrain	8 hr. 1 min.	568
23 Sept.	Bahrain, local (desert strip)	1 hr. 12 min.	
25 Sept.	Bahrain–Muscat (Seeb)	6 hr. 43 min.	523
26 Sept.	Muscat–Karachi	7 hr.	554
28 Sept.	Karachi–Delhi	9 hr. 5 min.	782
29 Sept.	Delhi–Agra	1 hr. 25 min.	118
30 Sept.	Agra, local (Taj Mahal)	1 hr. 9 min.	
30 Sept.	Agra–Delhi	1 hr. 50 min.	118
1 Oct.	Delhi–Calcutta	10 hr. 10 min.	820
3 Oct.	Calcutta–Rangoon	8 hr. 20 min.	686
4 Oct.	Rangoon–Bangkok	4 hr. 45 min.	374
5 Oct.	Bangkok–Langkawi	6 hr. 18 min.	515
6 Oct.	Langkawi, local	52 min.	
7 Oct.	Langkawi–Penang	1 hr. 10 min.	86
7 Oct.	Penang–Sitiawan	1 hr. 15 min.	98
7 Oct.	Sitiawan–Singapore (Seletar)	4 hr. 7 min.	308
9 Oct.	Singapore–Palembang	3 hr. 55 min.	276
9 Oct.	Palembang–crash site (Sumatra)	1 hr. 47 min.	140
16 Oct.	Crash site–Jakarta (Halim)	2 hr. 2 min.	136
18 Oct.	Jakarta–Kalijati–Jakarta	1 hr. 55 min.	124
19 Oct.	Jakarta–Surabaya	6 hr. 33 min.	414
20 Oct.	Surabaya–Bali	3 hr. 3 min.	208
20 Oct.	Bali–Bima	3 hr. 34 min.	237
21 Oct.	Bima–Kupang (Timor)	5 hr. 10 min.	368
22 Oct.	Kupang–Darwin	7 hr. 31 min.	518
Total		**148 hr. 35 min.**	**11,256**
			(not including local flights)

Vimy Specifications

	REPLICA NX-7IMY	ORIGINAL G-EAOU
Wingspan	68 ft.	same
Wing chord	10 ft. 6 in.	same
Wing area	1,376 sq. ft.	same
Length	43 ft. 6 1/2 in.	same
Height	16 ft. 4 in.	same
Tailspan	16 ft.	same
Wheel track	21 ft. 11 in. (outer)	same
	11 ft. 1 in. (inner)	same
Propeller (diameter)	10 ft. 8 in.	10 ft. 6 in.
Cruising speed	85 m.p.h.	same
Stall speed	45 m.p.h.	same
Average groundspeed en route	76 m.p.h.	83 m.p.h.
Weight (empty)	7,940 lb.	7,201 lb.
Weight (maximum)	12,637 lb.	12,500 lb.
Endurance	13.5 hr.	11 hr.
Fuel capacity	673 gal.	516 gal.
Total hours flown (UK–Australia)	148 hr. 35 min.	135 hr. 55 min.
Total miles (en route only)	11,256 miles	11,060 miles
Average miles per flying day	450 miles	461 miles
Engines	454 cu. in. Chevrolet V-8	Rolls Royce Eagle VIII V-12
First flight	July 30, 1994	October 3, 1919

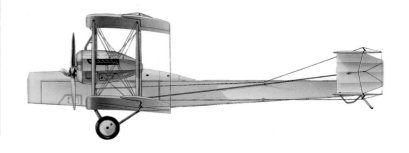

A FLYING LESSON

WHEN YOU WALK UP TO THE VIMY for your first flight, you can't help but be awed by the size of the machine. Stand by the wingtip, about head height for an average man, now look up, and you'll see the upper wing way up there, more than 16 feet off the ground. Move the massive aileron up and down. It's the same size as the entire wing of a Cessna 172. Walk around the tail, and you think you're seeing double—there's two of everything. Two rudders, two vertical fins, two elevators, two stabilizers. And all the control cables are external, so the rear fuselage looks like a giant guitar. Time to mount up.

ATHLETIC ENTRY

Rather than climb up the nose-skid for our first try, let's jump up on the trailing edge of the wing next to the fuselage. It's a big step, but you can pull yourself up by grabbing the rim of the rear cockpit, and then crawl up on the turtledeck. Step down into the pilot's cockpit. Settle into the left seat and acquaint yourself with the instruments. The engine gauges will take some getting used to: they're about 6 feet to your side, out on the cowls. Put your belts on first, then your helmet and goggles. Now let's go flying.

First make sure that both throttles, the black, knobbed levers between the seats down by your right hand, are closed. Make sure the number three fuel tank is on: that's the third red lever from the left under your seat. Now, go to the left side of the panel and turn both master switches on, then the fuel pumps, and select a computer for each engine, main or backup. Finally, turn on the left ignition and you'll hear a whirring sound. That's the fuel pump, which, as a safety precaution, doesn't come on until you're ready to start the engine. The fuel pressure gauge reads 48 psi, so push the big red button on the left. (The left is always started first, because the pilot has a clear view of that side.)

The big V-8 barks to life after only a few blades have gone past your ear, and she settles down to a nice rumble at about 1,100 RPM. Remember, the props are going only one-fourth that speed. Advance the throttle slightly so that the alternator kicks in. Now yell "Clear right!" and repeat the procedure on that side. The oil pressure should be about 65 psi, and let the radiator temp warm up to about 160 degrees Fahrenheit. Make sure the tailwheel is unlocked, and we're ready to taxi.

Use the throttles gingerly, because, weighing in at more than 10,000 pounds, she won't stop in a hurry. Keep that taxi speed down to a brisk walking pace. You can steer her side to side by using differential power from the engines. Move the wheel and the rudders, and check the action of the control surfaces. As heavy as you thought! Complete the preflight checks, and we'll be ready to line up on the runway.

Wiggle the rudders as you're rolling slowly forward until you're happy with the alignment. Now, reach down with your right hand and lock the tailwheel. Bring the power in smoothly, and you'll be surprised to find you're barely moving forward, even with full throttle. We're picking up speed, so keep it straight with the rudders—very effective. Ease the control wheel forward about 2 inches to get the tail up, unless there's a passenger in the bow (in which case hold back pressure throughout the takeoff or you may drag the nose-skid). While we went over that, you probably didn't notice that we're in the air already!

TWO-FISTED FLYING

We lifted off below 50 miles per hour, and now we're climbing at 400 feet per minute because we have only 200 gallons of fuel on board. Keep her climbing at 60 miles per hour, and don't attempt any turns yet, but see if you can synchronize the props. That's better: you can tell by the resonance beating on the side of your head. Level off at 1,500 feet and the airspeed will come up to 85 miles per hour. Ease the throttles back to about 3,800 RPM, and crane your neck to check the engine gauges. The fuel pressure is stable, and the water temp has come up to 180 degrees Fahrenheit. OK.

Now try a shallow turn to the left. Lead with the rudders and move the wheel slightly left. Whoa! Not what you expected! The nose pitched up and to the right. Did you notice that nothing happened when you first used the ailerons? That null area is because all four ailerons are floating up about 2 inches at the trailing edges when the plane is in flight. So you get no response at first, and then quite a bit when you roll the wheel into a turn.

Let me show you a trick. For a shallow turn to port, let's use a touch of right aileron and plenty of left rudder. See how much easier that is. For a steeper turn, we'll start the same way and then roll in some left aileron to set a 30-degree bank to the left. There's the angle of bank; now hold hard against it—harder! Don't let that bank steepen—the plane is dynamically unstable and will keep right on going unless you hold against the bank. Now lead with the right rudder to level the wings. She feels like an old mare, doesn't she. You can nudge her hard, but she still doesn't move in a hurry.

BACK TO EARTH

There's a slight breeze from the west, so we must land that way. Turning downwind, don't be alarmed, but if you get a gust on the tail, she'll feel like you've lost control. You're OK. It's just that the null area of the ailerons is much larger when a wind comes from behind. Use the controls aggressively. Although she is big, she is very slow, so the pattern is small.

Set up at 60 to 65 miles per hour and ease the power back to about 2,400 RPM. Much quieter. Listen to the music of the wires. The props are only at 600 RPM. You can almost count the blades! We are abeam the numbers at 800 feet, floating down at 300 feet per minute. It's better to make a continuous shallow turn rather a square base leg. Don't let her drift across the centerline.

Alignment looks good. At 300 feet, start easing off the power. You are gliding in a giant box kite. Use the rudders to pick up that wing drop. Over the numbers—now begin a gradual roundout. Keep the wheel coming back slowly, a few feet to go. Isn't it incredible how she floats! It's the ground effect from the massive wings. Forget about the airspeed indicator. Concentrate on attitude. Nose up a bit more—wheel in your lap. Whump! She's on…all the tires at once: a perfect five-point landing. Keep her straight. Tap dance on those rudders. Slow her down to walking pace. Now, unlock the tailwheel, and a burst of power from the right engine will turn her off the runway. Watch your arms when you're waving to your friends—those props are close. Good thing for those elbow guards. Shut off the switches and be careful getting down—it's a long drop. Jump down off the wing, take off your helmet and guess what—you're a Vimy pilot!

ACKNOWLEDGMENTS

SPECIAL THANKS TO THE FOLLOWING:

UNITED STATES
Walter J. Boyne; Chuck Williams; Aviation Methods, Inc.; Sheffield Engineering; Roger McMullen; Pat Healey; Chris and Carey Condy; Donald and Julie Munro; The William E. Simon and Carol G. Simon Foundation; Erin Porter; Eleanor Jones; Billy Campbell; Kim Arthur; Mike Balog; Ray Ledabrand; Ray Dolby; Don Lopez; Otto and Yvonne Tschudi; Francois Babel; John Skeen; Kim Bailie; Integral Partners; Jack Levin; Janet Green; Terry McGlinn; John Patten; Twan Chu; Joanne Coombs; Peter Holbrook; Ben Ostlind; Ted Wixted; George Williams; Patty Rebholz; Gary Meermans; Gary Kent; John Wilkinson; Federal Express; NAS, Brunswick, Maine; Allied Signal/Bendix-King Avionics; Perrone Leathers; Sigtronics; Bay Avionics

UNITED KINGDOM
Geoff Gregg; Tony Ditheridge; David, Joanna, Kate, Emma, Jim and Nick Lumsden; Norris McWhirter; Simon Gaul; Jean-Luc Aeby; Dominic Fry; John Sandford; Sir Richard Lloyd; Michael Farlam; Martin Brodie; Peter Boxer; Vic Parkes; Stephen Maycock; George Bacon; Anthony Hutton; Richard Vickery; Trafalgar House; Chris Warner; Robin MacKay; National Rescue; Andy Lambert; Paul Swift; Tony Amos; Michael Oakey; Norman Pealing; Ron Scobling; R. J. Kennett; McCarthy Weybridge: Ian Donabie; Jones Catering Hire: Jules Senior; Motor Way Ltd.: Tim Roberts; Ray Rimmell; Vickers P.L.C.; Rolls Royce P.L.C.; Museum of Science and Industry, London; Royal Air Force Museum, Hendon; Sotheby's, London

AUSTRALIA
Jodie Greer; Norman Pointing; Norm Worth; Audie Lloyd; C. K. Poultney; Dennis McNulty; Captain P. Schlossbermel; Captain Dick Hodder; Captain Russell Dann; Stan Letchford; Brian Shadler; John Martin; George Robertson; Coffs Harbour City Council; Peter Wilkinson; Berrima Aero Club; Bill Duff; Parkes Aero Club; Mike Stock; Dr. Austin Asche; Robyne Burridge; Wendy Miles; Narromine Aero Club; Narrandera Shire Council; Ken Murphy; Mr. and Mrs. J. Foley; John Hasted; Brian Shadler; Greg Ferguson; Longreach Shire Council; Moorooka Hyundai; Judy and Roy Riddel; Margaret Bridgman; Wendy Hall; Sue Burdekin; David Bell; Chris Ryland; Graham and Judy Sinclair; Rick Davies; Brigadier Rod Earle; Richard Phillips; Andrew Cranston; Wayne Schumacher; Bob Glindeman; Ian Kew; Chris Evans; Andrew Robson; Group Captain Mac Cottrell; Ken and Cynthia Rattey; George Brown; Ken Durwood; Andrew Holleyoak; Guy Cole; Royal Queensland Aero Club; Caboolture Aero Club; Glenda Duncan; Lil Hill; Mrs. Charles Huxtable, O.A.M.; Kylie Kidby; Katrina Kidby; Mr. and Mrs. G. Batten; Ms. E. Rawnsley; Mr. and Mrs. Duncan Fysh; Royal Victorian Aero Club; Garth Rhodes; Peter Cole; Ron and Neville Harvey; Peter Magarrey; Royal Newcastle Aero Club; Frank Pangello; Museum of Army Flying, Oakey, Queensland

FRANCE
Pol Roger Champagne; Bernard Hougouneng; Patrick Albrand; Michel Boutin; Ambassador Mark Pierce; Phillipe Trelliet; Groupe Accor

ITALY
General Domenico Mazza; Peter Scott King; James Halley; Captain Giovanni Giorgi; Captain Giuseppe Panico; Captain Bonita; Gregori Alegi; Commander LaSala; Gianni Bisogni; Giovanni Achbano; Aero Club di Roma

GREECE
Ambassador Thomas Niles; George Legakis; Larry Ikels; Michael Anthimos; A. Mouslidas; Alexis Laskaris

EGYPT
Ambassador C. E. McDonald; Paul Strickland; Satish Kumar; Riham el Aasar; Nile Valley Aviation; Mena House Oberoi

SAUDI ARABIA
HRH Prince Mogrin bin Abdulaziz Al Saud; His Excellency Hamad Rasheu Abu Nayyan; Ambassador Warwick Weemaes; Mohamed Ali Al Belehi; Ali Abdulaziz Al Qasim; Majeed Abdulaziz Al Aqeel; Mubarek N. Al Dossary; Abdullah Saleh Al Hagiri; Abdul Kerim Khatim Al Shammery; Ali Alqahtani

BAHRAIN
(*in addition to those mentioned on pages 10–11*)
Fathi Mattar; Clive Jacques; Jalal Qambar; Surbita D'Souze; Ahmed Al Ghani; Huider Ali; Abdul Khaliq Saeed; Alyson Evans; John Chisolm; Al-Hekma Model School

OMAN
Mohammed Ali Al Riyami; John Mills

PAKISTAN
Group Captain Graeme Carroll; Muhamed Murad; Fafar Khan; Sir Christopher MacRae; Eric Callaway

INDIA
P. R. S. Oberoi; Squadron Leader Kamal Deep; Wing Commander S. S. Ramerao; Ian Hughes; Jane Saberwahl; Group Captain John Bell; Darren Gribble; Kitty Tawakley; Barry Levin; Rajesh Chaturvedi; Atul Bindal; 29th Air Wing, Allahabad; Aeronautical Society of Calcutta

BURMA (MYANMAR)
Ambassador S. H. R. Hume; U. Thaung, Ambassador to USA; U. Thura Aung Htet; Franklin Huddle; Joan Philp; Ian Coghill

THAILAND
Ambassador David Lamberston; Novotel Siam Square; Robert Pounds

MALAYSIA
Melvyn Louis Mohamad Fazi; Aidi Abdullah; Roland Yap

SINGAPORE
Singapore Flying Club; Lee Buck Choon; Kevin Treloar; Novotel Orchid; Teoh Eng Hong; David Richards; Christopher Phua Chai; Chew Choong Cheng

INDONESIA
His Excellency Joop Ave; U. Suganda; David Bell; First Administrator Soedarko; H. M. Idris Prawarto; Drs. Hariyo Wibowo; C. L. Moncrieff; Skadron Tecknik 021; Drs. Hidayatullah; Letda Kornelis; I. Warsa; Bob Ingle; Brigadier Kerry Mellor; Adriani Ramelan; Heno Wahyuna

CONSTRUCTION
United States
(WOODWORK, FABRIC WORK, ELECTRICAL, FUEL SYSTEM, ASSEMBLY, AVIONICS, PAINTING, RIGGING)
REGULAR CREW: Jim Allen; Bev Kidby; Duncan Audette; Christian Bull; Beverley Esler; Jane Lucas; Erik Durfey; Ray Mandoux; Shawn Mulligan; Billy Freeman; Dan Nelson, Jr.; Doug Griffin; Ken Olson; Jay Jerde; D. Kendall Farley; Paul Goyetche; J. D. Durst; Orlandi's Auto
VOLUNTEERS: Bill Boitano; Tom and Linda McMillan; Dr. Thomas McMillan; Chris La Noue; Chris Barnes; Bob and Madeleine Hopkins; Ed Whyschmeyer; John Ford; Carol and Bob Wallerman; Brian Esler;

The team gathers for a final picture in Darwin shortly after arrival. Back row, left to right: Major Mick Reynolds, Malcolm Wood, Captain Gary Tierney, Peter McMillan, Mark Rebholz, Lang Kidby, Bev Kidby, Joe Stancampiano, Sean Maffett. Front row, left to right: (*inset*) Ian Snell (who had to return to the United Kingdom early after contracting a serious tropical illness), Corporal Bob Shaw, Dan Nelson, Bob Poole, Chris Weber, Mark Roy, Jim Stanfield.

Bill Totton; Ken Copp; Patty Rebholz; Ed Bullian; David Prinz

DESIGN AND CONSTRUCTION
Australia
(ENGINES, GEARBOXES, FUSELAGE, UNDERCARRIAGE, FUEL TANKS, STRUTS)
AIRCRAFT ENGINEERING: Clive Abraham; Mark Arnold; Dot Daley; Dr. Peter Dueker; John Anstam; Kylee Waite; Patrick Watson
DRAFTING STAFF: Ted Baker; Mark Compton; Daryl Christie; Jason Derry; Mike Jarvis; Matthew Tomson

COMPONENTS AND SERVICES
DONATED: *Avionics*: Allied Signal/Bendix-King/AWA, Inc.; Bay Avionics; *Intercoms/Headsets*: Sigtronics; Perrone Leathers; *Engine Mounts*: Sheffield Engineering
SUBCONTRACTED: *Flying Wires*: Bruntons (Musselburgh) Ltd., Scotland; *Propellers*: Dick Sweetapple, Australia; Richard Vickery, UK; *Wheels*: Dick Fischer, USA; Don McMakin, USA; *Engine Cowlings*: G. Williams, UK; Chris Barnes, USA; British Airways: Charles Brakespeare, Peter Norton, John Quinlisk; United Airlines; *Avionics*: Bay Avionics, USA; *Radiators/Fuel Lines*: Greg Hartwell, USA; *Fabric Work*: AJD Engineering, UK; *Nose-skid*: Robert Dunlop, Australia; *Precision Fabrication*: Ron Debruin, USA; *Bungee Cords*: Chris Rehage, Germany

PHOTO CREDITS
The following photographs are by courtesy of the National Geographic Society (t: top, b: bottom, c: center, l: left, r: right): 131b (John Clark Archer); 151t (Alexander Graham Bell); 119b, 125b (Boston Photo News Co.); 175b (Albert L. Godoy); 101b (N. H. Hampton); 93 (Earle Harrison); 68t (Frank Hurley); 171b (F. O. Koch); 167b (E. B. McDowell); 165c (Theodore Macklin); 109br, 113b (Donald McLeish); 209b (Henry Ruschin); 30–1, 47t, 50–1t, 52–4, 56, 59, 62, 63b,145, 149t, 185br, 203b, 205b, 213b, 215c, 227cr (Ross Smith); 117tr; 149t; 173cr; 193b; 195b.

All other photographs are by James L. Stanfield, National Geographic Society, except for the following: Bob Alford and Don Mutter: 48t; Australian Archives: 215br; Bruntons (Musselburgh) Ltd., Scotland: 237cl; Central Photographic Establishment and RAAF Museum Collection, Crown Copyright reserved: 10–11, 36, 37b, 47br, 57, 68–9b; Terry Gwynn-Jones: 32–4, 37t, 38–42, 44, 46t, 50b, 60–1, 70t, 70b, 71t, 72tl; Paul Hastings: 45, 46–7b, 69t, 75, 224l; Paul Hastings, courtesy Civil Aviation Historical Society (South Australia): 48b, 49, 63t, 63cr; George Herriman: 66t, 197b; Karl Horvatt: 55t; Hulton Deutsch: 43; Mrs. Charles Huxtable, O.A.M.: 55b; Garry James Collection: 67cl; John Oxley Library, Brisbane: 63tl; Susan R. Kline: 241tr; John La Noue: 232–3t, 243 (except tl and cr), 244, 245 (except cl), 246l, 247t, 248c, 248–9tc; Richard Leech: 252; Susan Leway: 231, 232cl; Peter McMillan: 72b; National Library of Australia, E. A. Crome Collection: 31, 32l, 67tr, 149b; Norman Pealing Ltd.: 76–7, 80–1, 82 (bl); Qantas Historical Collection: 35, 58, 64–5, 74c, 122t, 215t, 249br; Quadrant Picture Library: 240–1t; George Roberts: 66b; Geoffrey Shakerley: 70c; Ian Snell: 254r; Joe Stancampiano: 84t, 248tl, 249tr; State Library of New South Wales: 71b and 227b (Bicentennial Copying Project), 74t (Dixson Galleries), 73, 122b and 215bl (Mitchell Library: 215bl photographed by Peter Luck, © Commonwealth of Australia, published with permission); State Library of South Australia: 256; University of Adelaide, Barr Smith Library: 67b, 123; unknown source: 72tr; Christine Weber: 254; Bill Whitney: 232tl, 232b, 242.

INDEX